Performance Appraisals: A Collection of Samples

Assembled by the SHRM Information Center
2nd Ed., March 1996

SOCIETY FOR
HUMAN
RESOURCE
MANAGEMENT

The Society for Human Resource Management (SHRM), the leading voice of the human resource profession, represents the interests of more than 70,000 professional and student members from around the would. SHRM provides its membership with education and information services, conferences and seminars, government and media representation, and publications that equip human resource professionals for their roles as leaders and decision makers within their organizations. The Society is a founding member and Secretariat of the World Federation of Personnel Management Associations (WFPMA) which links human resource associations in 55 nations.

To order additonal copies of this publication, see page 270

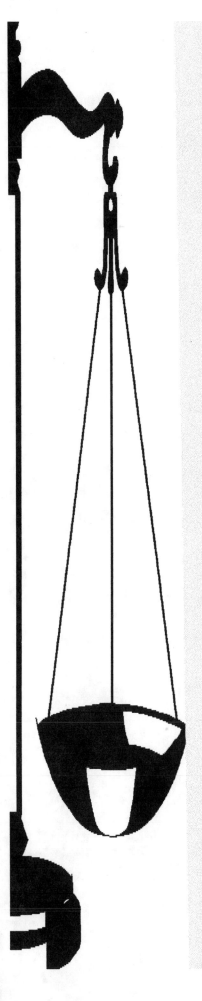

Table of Contents

I.   INTRODUCTION

In the Fall of 1995, after many requests from members for 360 degree review forms, and other "progressive" types of appraisals, the SHRM Information Center began working on a 2nd edition of our collection of samples. We requested sample forms from the members who have listed themselves under the member match topic of "Performance Appraisal". We received excellent responses and used many of the samples provided to compile this book. In addition to general performance appraisal forms, we have also included forms for the following types of reviews: seasonal, team, peer, upward, project/task management, competency/criteria-based, participative, exec./management, and 360 degree. Although the names of the companies have all been removed, these forms are intended as samples and should be adapted to your particular company's needs.

When designing a performance appraisal form, keep the following issues in mind:

- Is the performance appraisal easy to read and understand?

- Can you easily determine achievement based on the measurements used?

- Are there specific criteria by which each performance element can be evaluated?

- Is there a space to provide suggestions for improvement and/or career development recommendations?

- Does the form allow space for the employee's comments?

It is very important for supervisors to receive training on how to conduct the performance appraisal process. It is imperative that the performance appraisal process is an ongoing one and not just an event that occurs annually. If conducted properly, the performance appraisal provides the employee with reinforcement for successfully achieving goals and objectives, and it may be used to establish goals for increasing the employee's overall skills and performance.

Performance Appraisals: Sword Or Shield?

Jodi Trager Plavner

An effective performance appraisal system can help shield employers from costly litigation by providing well-documented, job-related reasons for personnel actions. In order to develop an effective and legal appraisal system, five basic steps must be followed. The first step involves the determination of exactly what purpose the performance appraisal system should serve. The second step, which is generally the most difficult and time consuming, is the selection of the criteria against which each employee will be evaluated. The third step is selecting the individuals who will perform the assessment function. The fourth step in the appraisal process is to train all of the individuals who will be acting as evaluators. The last step of the process is the counseling of each employee by the evaluator.

An appraisal system developed and implemented according to these five steps will help employers to avoid involvement in costly litigation brought by employees who allege that their status as an employee was affected due to their race, color, religion, age, sex, national origin or disability.

I. What Purpose Does An Appraisal System Serve?

A. Employee Motivation

Due to tough economic times many companies need to figure out additional ways to motivate employees without increasing costs. A performance appraisal system, if used correctly, can be the perfect motivational tool.

To increase employee motivation substantially, employers should make an effort to make each employee feel that he/she is an integral part of the company, a part of the decision making process and a valued link. Employers can do this by allowing employees to take part in goal setting with regard to performance and productivity expectations and by making sure that the company's expectations are clear and realistic. Employers who allow their employees to take part in the setting of performance goals typically find that their employees work harder to accomplish the goals and are more satisfied with their jobs.

B. Increase Productivity By Tying Compensation to Performance Appraisal

Many companies tie compensation to performance appraisal to encourage increased productivity and performance. When compensation is tied to performance, both courts and employees place extra attention on the actual review process. Hence, it becomes even more important for the performance reviews to accurately reflect an employee's performance and productivity. In addition, evaluators need to realize that employees may closely scrutinize the evaluator's written and oral words when their compensation is based in part or in whole on an evaluator's review.

Tying compensation to productivity is easier and safer in situations where an employee's productivity is clearly identifiable to the evaluator. For instance, in a plant situation, the productivity of each assembly line employee is easily measured based on the number of pieces he/she completes. However, in an office setting an employee's performance may be more difficult to measure. Decisions to compensate such an employee may not be as objective or seem as justifiable as in the assembly line situation. Employers who wish to tie compensation to performance reviews must realize that even when caution is taken to ensure fairness, employees still may become frustrated if their hard work is not rewarded to the extent they believe they are entitled.

C. Determining the Order of Layoff

The order of layoffs and/or an employee discharge can successfully be justified by employee performance evaluations. However, in order to use performance evaluations as a justification or as a defense, employers must make sure that the appraisal system is consistent, accurate and as objective as possible. If the employer claims that an employment decision was performance-based, the employee's performance reviews will be produced as justification. In this situation, the employer may find that the employee's performance reviews do not confirm that the employee was a poor performer. This is a common problem due to evaluators' tendencies to inflate employee evaluations. Hence, employers often lose discrimination cases because they cannot prove that their reason for making an employment decision was lawful and not merely a pretext for a discriminatory reason. Training of evaluators will help improve the accuracy of performance evaluations.

D. Tool for Succession Planning, Promotion and Demotion Decisions

Employers often neglect one of the most beneficial uses of performance appraisals, which is to guide succession planning.

Jodi Trager Plavner is an attorney in the Labor department of the Philadelphia law firm of Wolf, Block, Schorr & Solis-Cohen. Ms. Plavner represents clients in traditional labor and equal employment opportunity matters, and also specializes in workpalce safety (OSHA) and other areas of employment law.

Promoting from within is a very good policy in terms of employee motivation and can benefit a company because the employee already has a work record with the company. When a new position becomes available, the performance appraisal can be used to evaluate whether a current employee is qualified for a different position.

II. Performance Appraisal Criteria

Once an employer determines the objectives of an appraisal system, the employer must determine what criteria each employee will be evaluated against. Performance appraisal instruments often cause dissatisfaction. Dissatisfaction on the part of the employee receiving the review, dissatisfaction on the part of the individual conducting the review, dissatisfaction on the part of management and dissatisfaction on the part of the court who evaluates whether the reviews are discriminatory and whether the reviews can serve as justification for an employment decision. Some dissatisfaction can be alleviated if time is spent developing specific, job-related criteria for each job or job family. Vague, ambiguous criteria do not allow the evaluator to accurately appraise each employee, do not inform the employee of how to improve performance and cannot be used effectively by management as a guide in making employment decisions.

Three types of criteria are commonly used: trait, result-oriented and behavioral criteria. A basic understanding of the various types of criteria is necessary before an appraisal instrument can be developed.

Trait-based criteria are used by many employers when time and money are limited because one set of trait-based criteria can generally be used for all positions. A trait-based evaluation rates an employee's subjective character traits such as his/her "dependability", "initiative" or "creativity" and has relatively little to do with the specific job. Due to the ambiguous nature of the traits, employees have a difficult time learning how to improve their performance.

Justifying employment decisions based on a trait-based evaluation is an arduous task. If the criteria selected are too subjective, not only will the evaluation be worthless with regard to improving employee performance and motivation, but the evaluation could be rejected by a court. Courts have held that evaluations based on criteria such as, "general demeanor," "social behavior" and "adaptability" are too vague, while criteria such as "ability to plan," "initiation of projects" and "education", which are more objective, are more acceptable.

If a company is determined to use appraisals based on traits, each trait must be defined for both the evaluator and the employee. The evaluator must understand exactly how to evaluate each employee and the employee needs to understand exactly what the employer expects. Employers who wish to use trait-based performance appraisals as an aid in defending litigation brought by a disgruntled employee should consider developing separate trait appraisals for each specific job or job family and, if possible, should combine the trait-based criteria with behavioral criteria.

Result-oriented criteria which focus on an employee's production or the cost-related outcome of an employee's work is a second type of criteria which can be used to evaluate employees. A result-oriented appraisal, in conjunction with a reward system based on employee productivity, is often helpful for employers who wish to increase employee productivity. However, by focusing only on quantitative measures or outcomes many important factors of an employee's job performance are neglected. Succession planning will be difficult, if not impossible, and employees who are in positions where their productivity is dependent on other employees may be tempted to claim that their evaluations are unfair. This problem may be avoided or at least alleviated if employees are asked to take part in the goal setting process.

Result-oriented evaluations are usually much more objective then trait-based evaluations and are generally considered a lawful means of employee evaluation. The major problem with result-oriented evaluations is that they do not tell an employee how to increase productivity, but instead, only that productivity is low, average or high. Evaluators can minimize the negative effects of cost-related outcome evaluations by taking the time to counsel employees on how to improve their productivity and on how to perform their job at the level expected by the employer.

A third type of appraisal system is one based on very specific, job-related behavioral criteria. Behavioral criteria are more difficult to develop, but are often the best way to evaluate employees. The behavioral criteria selected must directly reflect the functions for which the employee is responsible. A different set of criteria is necessary for each position. To develop each evaluation instrument it is necessary to review the job description, if one exists, for the specific position.

An evaluation system based on specific behavioral criteria, if constructed correctly, serves as excellent written advice to employees regarding what management expects of them and informs them of how they are performing their job duties. After the evaluations are conducted, it is clear to management which employee could handle the job responsibilities of a different position.

Once the criteria for each evaluation instrument are selected the entire appraisal system should be pretested to determine if the system is practical, basically objective, lawful and effective. From a legal standpoint, the most important test is whether or not the criteria are job-related and objective. Performance evaluations can only be used to successfully justify a performance-related employment decision if the reviews are sufficiently detailed and job-related and if factors such as an employee's race, sex or age do not form the basis of any of the negative comments stated in the review.

III. Who Should Conduct Performance Appraisals?

Many attorneys, human resource professionals, employers and supervisors disagree as to who should perform the actual assessment function. Most commonly, employees are reviewed by their immediate supervisor and/or manager. However, while this may be the most common procedure, an employee's immediate supervisor may not be the only individual qualified to perform the evaluation and may not always be the best individual to perform the appraisal. An employee's supervisor, peers, subordinates or even the employee himself can serve as the appraiser as long as he/she is aware of the duties and responsibilities of the employee's job, and has observed the employee performing his duties on a frequent basis.

Recently, more companies have made use of peer review, and/or self-evaluation. A peer review system is one in which an employee's peers evaluate him/her based on an appraisal instrument created by the company. Peer review is a valid and effective way to appraise employee performance as long as an employee's peer(s) are familiar with the employee's performance. Many researchers have found that peer reviews are actually more consistent than reviews performed by an employee's supervisors.

Self-appraisal, which requires employees to evaluate themselves, forces employees to focus on what they believe management expects from them and on how well they are meeting management's expectations. Self-appraisals highlight the differences between what employees feel are their responsibilities and what their supervisors feel are their duties. A major problem with self-appraisals is that poor performers tend to inflate their reviews, while the hard workers tend to appraise themselves more honestly. If at all possible, it is best to combine the self-appraisal system with supervisory evaluations.

IV. What Training Should Evaluators Be Given?

The individuals who are expected to perform the appraisals need specific training on exactly how to conduct evaluations. Appraisers who are not trained often end up giving employees inflated reviews to avoid confronting an employee with negative comments. Inflated reviews may come back to haunt an employer who wishes to make an employment decision based on the performance of an employee, but who later realizes that the employee's past reviews are inaccurate. To avoid inflated reviews evaluators must be instructed to document specific examples of performance problems.

Evaluators should be trained to scrutinize their comments before verbalizing them or committing them to paper. While an evaluator may not intend to make a biased remark, he/she must be taught that many seemingly innocent remarks actually may be construed as discriminatory. The more subjective an evaluation is, the more susceptible it is to attack by a court. For instance, when a man is described as "aggressive," the connotation is generally positive. However, a woman with the same "aggressive" quality may be viewed in a negative manner, as "pushy" or "rough." If the man, based on his aggressive qualities is given the promotion, and the woman is denied a promotion because of her aggressive qualities, the reviews could serve as sufficient evidence to substantiate or defend a claim of discriminatory performance evaluation. While subjective comments are often unavoidable, evaluators need to document or substantiate their subjective comments with objective examples.

Although the evaluation form itself serves as an outline for employee performance reviews, training of supervisors is of equal importance to guarantee that the appraisal instruments are implemented correctly.

V. Counseling Employees

After the evaluator(s) complete an employee's appraisal and review it to make sure it accurately reflects the employee's performance, the evaluator(s) should set a time to meet with the employee to discuss the review. The meeting should be held on company property in a location where there will be no distractions. The evaluator should explain to the employee how the evaluation process works, what criteria the evaluation was based upon and how the employee has performed in relation to the criteria. Evaluators will find that their meetings with employees will go more smoothly if they begin each meeting by making a few positive comments about the employee's performance and then proceed in an objective, organized fashion, to discuss specific tasks, behaviors or responsibilities which the employee needs to improve. The evaluators should also take time to make suggestions on how each employee can work to successfully meet the expectations of management. Throughout the meeting, the evaluator should solicit comments and discussion from the employee. After the appraisal meeting is completed the evaluator and the employee should sign the review, indicating that the two individuals discussed the evaluation.

VI. Conclusion

If the five basic steps outlined above are followed, in conjunction with common sense, a company can use a performance appraisal system as a shield which will help them get the most from their employees and protect them from lawsuits which could cost the company legal fees, court costs, damages, time and effort. However, if companies are not willing to take the time and put in the necessary effort, an appraisal system can turn into a sword which can cause an employer harm when defending a lawsuit brought by an employee.

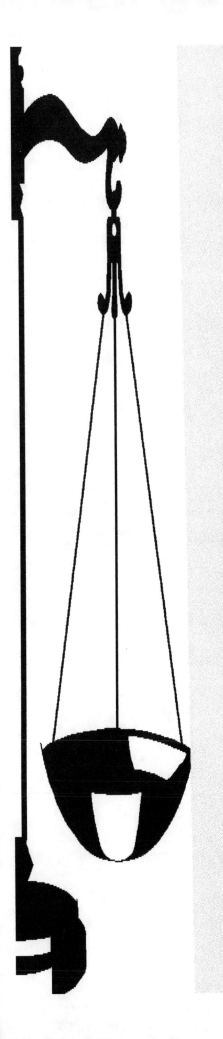

III.

General Performance Appraisals

8

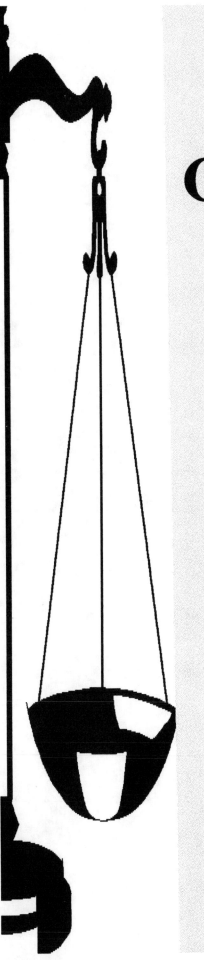

General Appraisal
#1

PERFORMANCE EVALUATION

Employee Name _____ Department _____ Review Date _____

Current Grade _____ Current Step _____ Current Rate _____ Employment Date _____ Change Effective Date _____

REVIEWER

Reviewer _____ Position Title _____

Report Based On
- ❑ Daily Contact
- ❑ Frequent Observation
- ❑ Infrequent Observation
- ❑ Other (Please Describe): _____

COMPENSATION REVIEW

Overall Performance Rating
- ❑ Outstanding
- ❑ Commendable
- ❑ Fully Competent
- ❑ Provisional (New Employee)
- ❑ Provisional (Experienced)
- ❑ Unsatisfactory

Action To Be Taken

❑ Step New Step: _____ New Rate:: _____

❑ Other * New Step: __NA__ New Rate: _____

Advancement to Steps 2 or 3 Requires a Provisional or Higher Rating. Advancement to Steps 4 and Above (and Bonus Eligibility) Require Fully Competent or Higher Ratings.

* New Step, Step Bonus and Longevity Bonus Do Not Apply

❑ Step Bonus $ _____ (X) Assigned Hours _____ (÷) 80 = $ _____ (Salary Range for Pay Grade)

❑ Longevity Bonus $ _____ (X) Assigned Hours _____ (÷) 80 = $ _____ (Sec VIII, Wage & Salary Manual)

Total Bonus $ _____

Comments/Notes/Special Instructions _____

AUTHENTICATION & APPROVAL

This evaluation has been discussed with me. I understand that a copy may be obtained from the Personnel Office. I further understand that my signature does not necessarily mean that I agree with this evaluation, and that it can be appealed through the Open Door Procedure (Personnel Policy #6-2).

Signature of Employee _____ Date _____

I have discussed this evaluation with the employee. I have also reviewed the enclosed Position Description/Performance Review form and have forwarded any recommended changes to the Personnel Office.

Signature of Reviewer _____ Date _____

Department Director _____ Date _____

Administrative Approval _____ Date _____

PERFORMANCE REPORT
(To Be Completed By Supervisor)

ACCOUNTABILITY	WEIGHT FACTOR		RATING		SCORE
(1)	_____	X	_____	=	_____
(2)	_____	X	_____	=	_____
(3)	_____	X	_____	=	_____
(4)	_____	X	_____	=	_____
(5)	_____	X	_____	=	_____
(6)	_____	X	_____	=	_____
(7)	_____	X	_____	=	_____
(8)	_____	X	_____	=	_____
(9)	_____	X	_____	=	_____
(10)	_____	X	_____	=	_____
(11)	_____	X	_____	=	_____
(12)	_____	X	_____	=	_____

TOTAL WEIGHT _____   TOTAL SCORE _____

TOTAL SCORE DIVIDED BY TOTAL WEIGHT _____

Weight Scale		Rating Scale		How Standards Met	
Most Critical	3	Outstanding	5	Review Policy	A
Important	2	Commendable	4	Direct Observation	B
Supportive	1	Fully Competent	3	Video Review	C
		Provisional	2	Skills Lab	D
		Unsatisfactory	1	Other (Specify)	E

Level of Experience/Expertise
1 = Little or None   2 = Some (May Require Pratice/Assistance)
3 = Competent and Experienced   4 = Able to Assess Competency of Others

SUPERVISOR'S DESCRIPTION OF OVERALL PERFORMANCE

_____

_____

_____

_____

_____

_____

_____

_____

POSITION REVIEW
(To Be Completed By Employee)

ENVIRONMENTAL RATINGS

	EXCELLENT	GOOD	FAIR	POOR	N/A
Your Salary	☐	☐	☐	☐	☐
Employee Benefits	☐	☐	☐	☐	☐
Other Employees	☐	☐	☐	☐	☐
Supervision	☐	☐	☐	☐	☐
Administration	☐	☐	☐	☐	☐
Communications	☐	☐	☐	☐	☐
Your Job Duties	☐	☐	☐	☐	☐
Job Safety	☐	☐	☐	☐	☐
Employee Facilities	☐	☐	☐	☐	☐
Employment Security	☐	☐	☐	☐	☐
Recognition of Efforts	☐	☐	☐	☐	☐
Workload	☐	☐	☐	☐	☐
Working Conditions	☐	☐	☐	☐	☐
Fair Treatment	☐	☐	☐	☐	☐
Policies/Procedures					
Hospital	☐	☐	☐	☐	☐
Department	☐	☐	☐	☐	☐

COMMENTS

_____

How well does your position satisfy your personal/professional goals?

_____

_____

_____

What would you like to see changed/improved?

_____

_____

_____

What training, career or future job opportunities are of interest to you?

_____

_____

_____

Please summarize your thoughts/feelings about your employment with Hannibal Regional Hospital:

_____

_____

_____

Signature of Employee _____ Date _____

PROGRESS

How well has employee accomplished the goals agreed upon at the time of last review?

_____

_____

_____

_____

_____

_____

DEVELOPMENT

State the agreed upon goals to be accomplished during the next rating period. Include agreed upon actions and time frames to be observed in attaining these goals:

Goals (Improvement/Achievement)	Actions/Objectives (Employee)	Actions/Objectives (Reviewer)	To Be Completed (Mo/Yr)

What steps can employee take to prepare for or enhance opportunities for future advancement? Include actions to be taken by reviewer to assist employee in accomplishing these steps:

_____

_____

_____

_____

EMPLOYEE COMMENTS CONCERNING PERFORMANCE REPORT/PROGRESS/DEVELOPMENT

_____

_____

_____

_____

_____

_____

_____

_____

PERFORMANCE LEVELS

Unsatisfactory

Performance is <u>inadequate</u> (below minimum acceptable standards and expectations). Performance is causing problems/inconveniences/hardships for the department and/or co-workers and is having a negative impact on departmental effectiveness and/or productivity. This level of performance cannot be condoned or allowed to continue. Employees with an overall rating of Unsatisfactory are not eligible for step/merit increases or bonuses.

Provisional (New Employee)

New employees are not expected to perform at the Fully Competent level required of more seasoned and experienced individuals. The new employee may need to be oriented to the job, complete required training and/or need time to become proficient through practice and/or exposure to the new working environment. This level of performance applies to the new employee who is essentially satisfying the standards and expectations of a person learning or becoming oriented to the new position. New employees performing at this level may progress to Steps 2 and 3 of their pay grade but must attain a Fully Competent or higher rating to progress beyond Step 3 and to be eligible for performance and/or longevity bonus.

Provisional (Experienced Employee)

Performance only meets the minimum standards and expectations. Performance is generally "acceptable" - but improvement is needed and expected. Performance at this level may cause the department and/or co-workers some problems or inconveniences - or tends to diminish the department's effectiveness and/or productivity. Performance at this level is characterized as "just getting by." Experienced employees assigned to Step 3 or higher in their pay grade, who receive an overall rating of Provisional, are not eligible for step/merit increases or performance and/or longevity bonus.

Fully Competent

Performance fully meets standards and expectations, and is GOOD - not AVERAGE. The individual performing at this level is considered a stable and skilled performer by co-workers and immediate supervision. Performance, at times, may be higher or lower - but averages to the Fully Competent level.

Commendable

Performance EXCEEDS standards and expectations. Performance at this level would generally be recognized by peers and immediate supervision. Performance is characterized by notable skill, initiative and superior job knowledge. This individual's performance exceeds most other employees in the same position.

Outstanding

Performance SIGNIFICANTLY EXCEEDS standards and expectations. Performance at this level would generally be recognized by peers, immediate supervision, lighter level management and others. The individual suggests and initiates improvements/changes and through his/her own performance has materially enhanced effectiveness of the department or work area. Performance is generally not equaled by others (current and/or former employees in the same position).

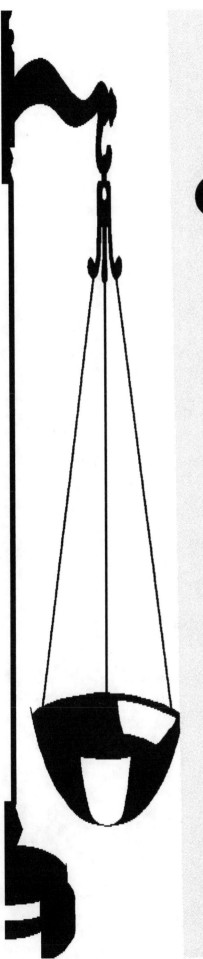

General Appraisal #2

EMPLOYEE PERFORMANCE APPRAISAL *(non-exempt)*

NAME _____   DEPARTMENT _____

JOB TITLE _____   DATE IN POSITION ___/___/___

APPRAISAL PERIOD: FROM ___/___/___ TO ___/___/___

APPRAISAL
PREPARED BY: _____   DATE APPRAISAL GIVEN ___/___/___

The evaluator's immediate supervisor and Human Resources must review the contents of the appraisal before the appraisal is conducted with the employee.

NEXT LEVEL APPROVAL _____   DATE ___/___/___

HUMAN RESOURCES APPROVAL _____   DATE ___/___/___

I participated in the Employee Performance Appraisal with my supervisor on the date indicated. The content of the appraisal has been discussed with me in detail.

My signature indicates knowledge and understanding of the contents of the appraisal and does not necessarily imply agreement.

EMPLOYEE SIGNATURE _____   DATE ___/___/___

EVALUATOR SIGNATURE _____   DATE ___/___/___

LEVELS OF PERFORMANCE

Outstanding	Performance and results achieved **always exceed** the standards and expectatons for the position requirements, performance standards and long & short-term objectives.
Exceeds Standards	Performance and results achieved **consistently exceed** the standards and expectations for the position requirements, performance standards and long & short-term objectives.
Meets Standards	Performance and results achieved **generally meet** the standards and expectations for the position requirements, performance standards and long & short-term objectives.
Below Standards	Performance and results achieved **generally do not meet** the standards and expectations for the position requirements, performance standards and long & short-term objectives.
Unsatisfactory	Performance and results achieved **consistently do not meet** the standards and expectations for the position requirements, performance standards and long & short-term objectives.

EMPLOYEE PERFORMANCE REVIEW RATING FORM

OBJECTIVES & PERFORMANCE FACTORS	A (3)	B (2)	C (1)
1.			
2.			
3.			
4.			
5.			
6.			
7.			
8.			
9.			
10.			
11.			
12.			
14.			
15.			
16.			
17.			
18.			
19.			
20.			

LEVEL OF PERFORMANCE	POINTS
OS - OUTSTANDING	5
ES - EXCEEDS STANDARDS	4
MS - MEETS STANDARDS	3
BS - BELOW STANDARDS	2
US - UNSATISFACTORY	1

TOTAL PRIORITY ITEMS	WEIGHTED FACTOR	WEIGHTED TOTAL
(A)	X 3	
(B)	X 2	
(C)	X 1	
	GRAND TOTAL ITEMS	

TOTAL PRIORITY POINTS	WEIGHTED FACTOR	WEIGHTED TOTAL
(A)	X 3	
(B)	X 2	
(C)	X 1	
	GRAND TOTAL POINTS	

OPTIONS:
1. Prioritize all items as A's, B's or C's.
2. Prioritize <u>objectives</u> as A's, B's or C's and prioritize all <u>performance factors</u> as C's for equal weighting.

Total Points:_____ divided by Total Items:_____ = Overall Rating Factor:_____

Present Salary:$_____ X Merit Increase % of _____ = $ _____

Effective Date: ___/___/___
       (mondays)

Date Of Next Review:___/___/___

Name: _____

Time on Job: _____

Job Title: _____

Grade:_____

RATESHT/03-94

PERFORMANCE FACTORS

RATE EACH CATEGORY SEPARATELY -- Include supporting comment
and/or demonstrated example to support rating given.

(OS = Outstanding   ES = Exceeds Standards   MS = Meets Standards
BS = Below Standards   US = Unsatisfactory)

OS	ES	MS	BS	US
(Check one)				

JOB KNOWLEDGE & COMPREHENSION: Understands and is knowledgeable of the
duties, methods and procedures required by the job. **PRIORITY: A B C (Circle one)**

_____

_____

WORK QUALITY: Completes work assignments thoroughly and completely in an
accurate, prompt, neat manner, including standards for verbal/written communications,
if applicable. **PRIORITY: A B C (Circle one)**

_____

_____

_____

PRODUCTIVITY: Produces required volume of work. Maintains attention to work and
meets deadlines. **PRIORITY: A B C (Circle one)**

_____

_____

_____

ACCURACY: Identifies and corrects errors. Is careful, alert and accurate, paying
attention to details of the job. **PRIORITY: A B C (Circle one)**

_____

_____

_____

WORK HABITS: Demonstrates commitment, dedication, cooperation, positive
behavior, adaptability and flexibility with changes in jobs and duties. Considers safety of
self and others while working. Takes accountability for job responsibilities.
PRIORITY: A B C (Circle one)

_____

_____

_____

INITIATIVE/PROBLEM SOLVING/ DECISION MAKING: Performs with minimal
supervision, acts promptly, seeks solutions to resolve unexpected problems that arise on
the job, makes practical, routine decisions. **PRIORITY: A B C (Circle one)**

_____

_____

_____

INTERPERSONAL SKILLS: Demonstrates ability to get along with others, is
respectful of co-workers, communicates and acts as a team player, promotes teamwork.
Responds and acts appropriately to confrontational situations.
PRIORITY: A B C (Circle one)

_____

_____

_____

ATTENDANCE & PUNCTUALITY: Dependable, arrives at work on time, reports on all
scheduled days, adheres to break and meal schedules.
NUMBER OF OCCURRENCES in the past 12 months: **Absences _____ Tardies _____**
PRIORITY: A B C (Circle one)

_____

_____

TOTAL OVERALL RATING:

      Overall Performance Rating Factor _____

Overall Summary of Performance/Additional Comments

_____
_____
_____
_____
_____
_____
_____
_____
_____

Significant Strengths/Accomplishments/Contributions

_____
_____
_____
_____
_____
_____
_____
_____
_____
_____

Opportunities for Improvement/Expectations for the next review period/Recommendations for future development

_____
_____
_____
_____
_____
_____
_____
_____
_____

Employee Comments/Feedback

_____
_____
_____
_____
_____
_____
_____
_____

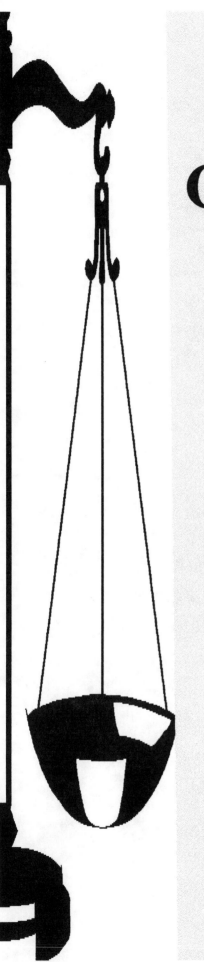

General Appraisal #3

Performance appraisal	
Employee	
Date	

Present job title	
Supervisor's name	

Importance of attribute in job

10   Essential to successful execution of job function
5   Important to successful execution of job function
0   Not required for execution of job function

Rating of employee for attribute

10   Excellent performance
9   Superior performance
8   Satisfactory performance
7   Some improvement desirable
6   Improvement required
4   Considerable improvement required
2   Needs urgent, major improvement

Ratings under 7 require a comment describing suggested improvement.

Work Performance

Customer service skills	Importance	Rating	Future	Comments
Develop customer (internal and external) relationships by making efforts to listen to and understand the customer; Anticipating and providing solutions to customer needs; Giving high priority to customer satisfaction.				

Quality	Importance	Rating	Future	
Accomplishing tasks through concern for all aspects of job; Accurately checking processes and tasks; Handling issues in a timely manner.				

Judgement and problem solving	Importance	Rating	Future	Comments
Committing to an action in a timely manner after developing alternative courses of action that are based on logical assumptions.				

Analysis and problem assessment	Importance	Rating	Future	Comments
Securing relevant information and identifying key issues and relationships from a base of information; Relating and comparing data from different sources; Identifying cause and effect relationships.				

Teamwork and collaboration	Importance	Rating	Future	Comments
Working effectively with team / work group to accomplish organizational goals; Taking actions that respect the needs and contributions of others; Contribution to, accepting and owning team decisions;				

Planning & organizing / work management	Importance	Rating	Future	Comments
Establishing a course of action for self and / or others to accomplish a specific goal; Planning proper assignments of personnel and appropriate allocation of resources; Completing tasks in allocated time and cost constraints.				

Revision 1, 3 July 1995

Technical / professional knowledge	Importance	Rating	Future	Comments
Achieving a satisfactory level of technical and professional skills or knowledge; Keeping abreast of current developments and trends in area of expertise; Familiarity and expertise in use of computer tools.				
Initiative	Importance	Rating	Future	Comments
Making active attempts to influence events to achieve goals; Self-starting rather than accepting passively; Taking action to achieve goals beyond what is required; Being proactive				
Individual leadership / influencing	Importance	Rating	Future	Comments
Using empowering interpersonal styles and methods to inspire and guide individuals (subordinates, peers and supervisors) toward goal achievement; Modifying behavior to accommodate tasks, situations and individuals involved.				
Strategic leadership	Importance	Rating	Future	Comments
Creating and achieving a desired future through influence on organizational values, individual and group goals, processes and procedures.				
Professional responsibility	Importance	Rating	Future	Comments
Accepting responsibility for tasks and personally committing to achieving goals; Professional resolution of work environment issues, concerns or interpersonal problems;				
Work ethic	Importance	Rating	Future	Comments
Time keeping, attendance; Attitude to work, company, colleagues; Reliability; Personal appearance.				
Communication	Importance	Rating	Future	Comments
Oral communication Written communication Written reports				
Innovation	Importance	Rating	Future	Comments
Creation of innovative solutions to technical problems;				
Assessment				

Achievements over review period

Revision 1, 3 July 1995

Technical skills

AutoCAD	Importance	Rating	Future	Comments
General proficiency				
Solids AME				
Drafting				
Graphic illustration, rendering				
Drawing file management				
Customizing, programming, maintenance				

Mechanical design	Importance	Rating	Future	Comments
Mechanisms				
Sheet metal				
Fabrications				
Tooling				
Workshop practices				

Electrical design	Importance	Rating	Future	Comments
Electrical systems				
Electronics (board level)				
Control systems				
Motion control				
Schematics				

Software	Importance	Rating	Future	Comments
Low level routines				
Visual Basic				
LONworks				
PLC ladder logic				

General skills	Importance	Rating	Future	Comments
Internal company procedures				
Computer tools eg Excel, Word				
Using company database				

Special skills	Importance	Rating	Future	Comments
LCD equipment and processes				
Mathematical analysis				
Vision systems				
Optics				
Assessment				

Notes

1. "Importance" indicates the importance of the attribute in the employee's job function over the review period.
2. "Rating" is the supervisor's assessment of the employee's performance. Most ratings will be in the region of 7 - 8, indicating there is some room for improvement.
3. "Future" indicates the importance of the attribute in the employee's job function in the next review period.
4. Importance and future assessment percentage shows the percentage of all listed skills applicable to the job function.
5. Rating assessment percentage is calculated as Sum(Rating * Importance / 10) / Sum(Importance) ie. an importance weighted rating. Most people should achieve a rating above 70%.

Employee's signature

Date

Supervisor's signature

Date

Revision 1, 3 July 1995

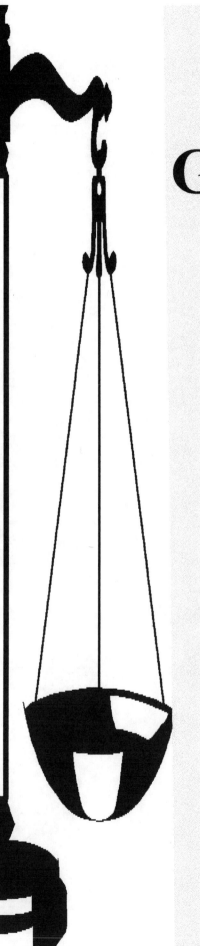

General Appraisal #4

PERFORMANCE SUMMARY

FOR SUPPORT STAFF

Name _____

Title _____

Division _____

Performance Period _____

Date of Discussion _____

Performance Summarized By _____

Date _____

My signature acknowledges that this performance summary has been discussed with me.

| _____ | _____ | _____ | _____ |
| Employee Signature | Date | Evaluator Signature | Date |

INSTRUCTIONS

I. OBJECTIVES

1. The performance summary is designed to provide employees of the National Kidney Foundation with feedback relating to individual strengths and areas requiring growth during each six months of their employment.

2. The performance summary is designed to stimulate dialogue between the staff member and the supervisor, and to encourage both parties to commit to goals to be accomplished during the next six months. It is intended to merely formalize a feedback process which is continually occurring between the employee and the supervisor. This process should be a comfortable experience for both parties.

II. RESPONSIBILITIES

1. In the Affiliate, the Executive Director should establish the process for all staff except himself/herself. The Executive Director's evaluation should be conducted by a committee of one to three volunteers. Recommended members of this group are the President, Immediate Past President, and incoming President. When the Affiliate has both a Chairman and a President, it is the Chairman who should participate in this process. They should offer the opportunity to the Executive Committee to provide input by announcing that an evaluation process will be taking place.

2. The Affiliate's Personnel Committee facilitates the process and offers the Affiliate President or Chairman guidance and instructions regarding the use of the evaluation tool. The Personnel Committee also reacts to what happens in the process. The appraisal process should be based on the Affiliate's planning process so clear goals can be set for the employee against which his progress can be measured; the performance discussion will focus on whether or not he has accomplished the agreed upon goals.

3. It is recommended that the performance discussion take place twice a year. In the first quarter, the discussion should include goal setting with each employee. Six months later, a performance discussion should be scheduled. The original performance discussion form should be reviewed and updated, and goals can be adjusted based upon this discussion.

III. PROCESS

1. The performance summary document should be given to staff to acquaint them with the new tool and to provide them the opportunity to consider their personal goals and objectives for the coming year.

2. The supervisor and the employee, independently, complete the document. It is not necessary that every item be discussed, only those that are applicable. Bulleted items present concepts to think about and should be responded to in a more global sense on the right hand side of the page.

3. The supervisor and the individual staff member meet and establish final goals and objectives. The supervisor reviews general management expectations and personal effectiveness. Both supervisor and employee sign a final document. The employee's signature acknowledges that the performance summary was discussed with him or her. Signing the form simply acknowledges that its contents were discussed; it does not necessarily mean the employee is in agreement with its contents. The supervisor's form is finalized and after review by the Executive Director becomes part of the personnel file

4. At the six month review date, the file copy of the performance summary is reviewed by the supervisor and employee. Goals and objectives are updated if needed based on this discussion.

5. At the 12 month annual review date, the evaluation process is repeated, with a final annual review form becoming part of the employee file.

SUPPORT EXPECTATIONS

PERFORMANCE DISCUSSION

I. DEPENDABILITY

- Attendance/Punctuality
- Follow through on assignments
- Meeting deadlines
- Assignments are complete

PERFORMANCE DISCUSSION

II. CUSTOMER/STAFF RELATIONS

- Deals tactfully & effectively with differences of opinion
- Creates effective relationships with staff & volunteers
- Assures internal & external "customer" responsiveness
- Acts in an ethical & appropriate manner

III. QUALITY OF WORK

- Accuracy
- Completeness
- How well work procedures are followed
- Reduces or eliminates avoidable costs or errors
- Initiates efforts in quality improvement

PERFORMANCE DISCUSSION

IV. ADAPTABILITY

- Moves from task to task readily
- Takes new circumstances in stride
- Is perceptive of impact and can modify behavior
- Is open to new ideas

PERFORMANCE DISCUSSION

V. TEAMWORK

- Accepts and uses suggestions for improvement
- Carries own share of responsibility
- Offers assistance & acknowledges other's work needs
- Resolves conflicts in an appropriate manner
- Initiates efforts to create an effective team

PERFORMANCE DISCUSSION

VI. DECISION-MAKING

- Takes appropriate action
- Identifies, chooses & balances needs & alternatives
- Knows when to shift decisions to another level
- Recognizes issues & requirements of problems

PERFORMANCE DISCUSSION

VII. COMMUNICATION

PERFORMANCE DISCUSSION

- Shares information completely
- Provides relevant, timely & accurate information
- Expresses ideas clearly in written & oral form
- Follows oral & written directions completely

VIII. ORGANIZATION

PERFORMANCE DISCUSSION

- Sets priorities
- Plans an approach before taking action
- Works without close supervision
- Work area is well organized
- Uses procedures & resources appropriately

ASSISTANCE NECESSARY TO FACILITATE MORE SUCCESSFUL PERFORMANCE:

MID YEAR PROGRESS REVIEW:

(This section filled out at 6 month progress review. Adjustments to goals may be made at this time.)

_____   _____

Employee Signature   Date

_____   _____

Evaluator's Signature   Date

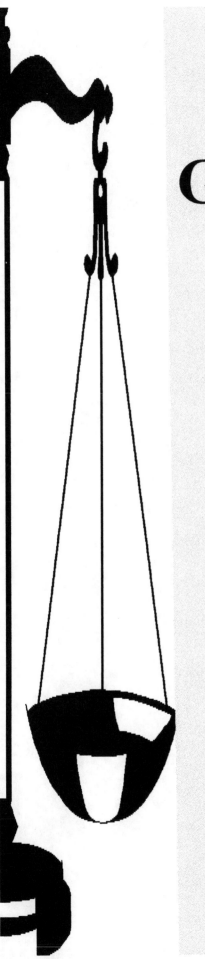

General Appraisal #5

LOGO

Name _____

Title _____

Unit _____

Time in Position _____

Review of Performance for the period _____ to _____

GUIDELINES FOR EVALUATING PERFORMANCE

The following recommendations are designed to assist you in evaluating the performance of your employees:

1. Upon receipt of this form, advise the employee of your approximate evaluation timetable so that he or she may also prepare. Encourage the employee's participation.

2. Complete this form considering the employee's performance during the entire review period. Evaluate performance using the following ratings:

   MARGINAL: Performance is clearly below the level of acceptability. This rating describes performance which has not kept pace with changing requirements, successes which have been only occasional, or performance which has been deteriorating. It may also describe the performance of a new employee who has not yet learned the fundamentals of the job. (Individuals with ratings in this category should either move up in performance level or out of the position in a short period of time.)

   ADEQUATE: Performance is below accepted levels for the time in position. This rating describes performance which meets only the very minimum position requirements and which could be improved through development, experience, and/or application.

   PROFICIENT: Performance is fully acceptable and results are achieved. This rating describes performance which demonstrates the required skills and knowledge for the position and sometimes exceeds expectations.

   COMMENDABLE: Performance is *consistently* above requirements. This rating describes performance which regularly exceeds expectations and demonstrates the willingness to assume additional responsibilities. This rating may also be used as special recognition for extraordinary performance which has significant impact on the organization.

3. Schedule a specific time for the performance evaluation meeting, assuring privacy without interruptions.

4. Conduct the evaluation discussion:
   - explain the purpose and your agenda
   - encourage response from the employee and two-way communication
   - mutually review performance expectations
   - discuss your ratings using specific examples
   - recognize areas of achievement and identify opportunities for improvement
   - explore career progress and determine developmental needs
   - plan performance goals for the next review period

5. Encourage the employee to make written comments and secure the employee's signature.

6. Forward the completed performance evaluation form to the Personnel Office.

PCS/PE4 Rev 94

EVALUATION OF KEY RESPONSIBILITIES

Review the employee's Position Description and evaluate performance in relation to position requirements.

1. _____

MARG	ADEQ	PROF	COMM

_____

_____

2. _____

MARG	ADEQ	PROF	COMM

_____

_____

3. _____

MARG	ADEQ	PROF	COMM

_____

_____

4. _____

MARG	ADEQ	PROF	COMM

_____

_____

5. _____

MARG	ADEQ	PROF	COMM

_____

_____

6. _____

MARG	ADEQ	PROF	COMM

_____

_____

Use insert if necessary to evaluate additional responsibilities.

EVALUATION OF GOALS/OBJECTIVES

Review business and behavioral goals for this review period, evaluate results achieved, and identify goals to be met within the next review period.

1. Present Review Period: _____

MARG	ADEQ	PROF	COMM

_____

_____

_____

2. Next Review Period: _____

_____

_____

_____

PERFORMANCE FACTORS

Review the following factors in relation to performance of job duties and make specific comments in support of the rating selected:

QUALITY:

MARG	ADEQ	PROF	COMM

How does it compare with accepted performance standards? Does it reflect sound job knowledge and sensitivity to client needs?
Comments: _____
_____
_____

QUANTITY:

MARG	ADEQ	PROF	COMM

How much acceptable work is produced in relation to anticipated deadlines and the employee's prior experience on similar assignments? Comments: _____
_____
_____

USE OF WORK TIME:

MARG	ADEQ	PROF	COMM

How well does the employee utilize available time in performance of responsibilities?
Comments: _____
_____
_____

INTERPERSONAL RELATIONS:

MARG	ADEQ	PROF	COMM

How well does the employee work and deal with others to accomplish job requirements?
Comments: _____
_____
_____

COMMUNICATIONS:

MARG	ADEQ	PROF	COMM

How effectively does the employee handle internal and/or external communications?
Comments: _____
_____
_____

DEPENDABILITY:

MARG	ADEQ	PROF	COMM

To what extent can the employee be relied upon to complete assignments within quality, budget, and time requirements?
Comments: _____
_____
_____

Please complete the following for this review period:

ATTENDANCE RECORD: _____ absences, totaling _____ days lost
PUNCTUALITY: Late _____ times (includes returning late from lunch/breaks)
VACATION: _____ days taken, _____ days carried forward

SPECIAL ACCOMPLISHMENTS:

Describe any accomplishments or special achievements which had significant impact on the department or organization.

_____
_____
_____

SUMMARY COMMENTS

Summarize the employee's overall performance including strengths and areas for improvement.

_____

_____

_____

_____

_____

_____

OVERALL PERFORMANCE RATING *(Select One)*

MARG	ADEQ	PROF	COMM

PROFESSIONAL DEVELOPMENT REVIEW

1. List any training programs, conferences or courses attended this year to improve present job skills, or for career development:

_____

_____

_____

_____

2. Identify possible developmental steps for this employee to improve in present job and/or prepare for future responsibilities:

_____

_____

_____

_____

EMPLOYEE COMMENTS

_____

_____

_____

_____

_____

_____

_____	_____
Employee's Signature	*Date*

_____	_____	_____	_____
Supervisor's Signature	*Date*	*Officer's Signature*	*Date*

44

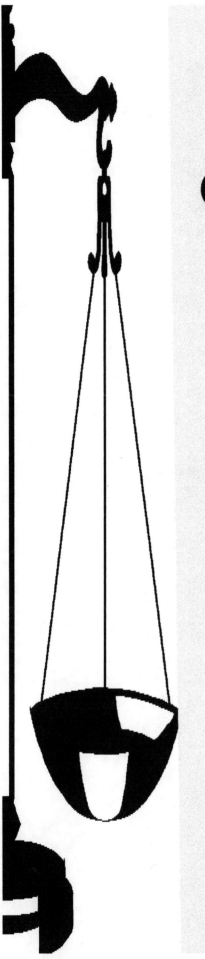

General Appraisal
#6

Performance Planning and Review Program

(For Salary Grades 4 - 13)

_____
Date

```
┌─────────────────────────────────────────────────┐
│ Planning and Review Information Concerning:       │
│                                                   │
│ Name _____          │
│                                                   │
│ Title _____          │
│                                                   │
│ Period Covered _____          │
└─────────────────────────────────────────────────┘
```

INSTRUCTIONS

1. Just prior to the end of the year write your performance objectives for the coming year on page 2 and obtain approval of your immediate superior. You and your superior and the next level manager sign on page 2. This form goes to your superior but you keep a copy.

2. At mid-year you meet with your superior for a review of your progress to date. You can meet more frequently if you both desire. Your superior records each progress review on page 2.

3. At the end of the plan year, you complete the Degree of Accomplishment section, page 2 and meet with your superior for your formal appraisal review. Your superior will have completed page 3 and you will jointly complete page 4 during the appraisal review. You and your superior and the next level manager sign on page 4.

Performance Standards

Outstanding Performance

Performance of assigned duties and results achieved greatly exceed average expectations. Performance is markedly superior to that of similarly classified employees in the company.

Good Performance

Performance of assigned duties and results achieved are measurably above average expectations. Performance is above that of similarly classified employees in the company.

Satisfactory Performance

Performance of assigned duties and results achieved are adequate with no serious failings. Any performance problems should be corrected through additional training and experience. Performance is average when measured against similarly classified employees in the company.

Marginal Performance

Performance of assigned duties and results achieved fall short of minimum expectations. Several serious or many minor failings. Performance is considerably below that of similarly classified employees in the company.

SECTION I

Performance Objectives

Instructions to Employee:

For each of your major areas of job responsibility, list in the Performance Objectives column below your objectives for the coming year. Your objectives should be specific and measurable.

Review these objectives with your immediate superior making any necessary changes. Leave this form with your superior, but keep a copy for your files.

Performance Objectives	Degree of Accomplishment

_____   _____

Agreed to: (Employee)   Date

_____   _____

Agreed to: (Immediate Superior)   Date

_____   _____

Approved by: (Next Level Manager)   Date

Progress Reviews

Record each occasion when progress is reviewed with employee. This must be done at least once a year. Indicate any changes made in performance objectives.

_____   _____
                                                   Date
_____   _____
                                                   Date

Unanticipated Accomplishments/Problems

Indicate any unforeseen opportunities realized and/or problems encountered and how dealt with:

_____

_____

SECTION II

Code: 1. Outstanding
2. Good
3. Satisfactory
4. Marginal

1. **Planning and Decision Making**
Was work well-planned and were decisions made promptly?What was the quality of the decisions?

1	2	3	4

_____

_____

_____

_____

2. **Organizing and Executing**
Was work well-organized and performed effectively and efficiently?

1	2	3	4

_____

_____

_____

_____

3. **Quality of Work**
How did the quality of work compare with standards of performance?

1	2	3	4

_____

_____

_____

_____

4. **Developing Employees**
Was the selection, motivation and development of subordinates effectively performed? Were tasks delegated and was there follow-up?

1	2	3	4

_____

_____

5. **Overall Evaluation**
The overall evaluation represents a composite of your evaluation of this individual's activity in the job during the appraisal period. Other comments on performance.

1	2	3	4

_____

_____

_____

SECTION III

TRAINING NEEDS ASSESSMENT

Place a checkmark in the appropriate block to indicate whether, in your judgement, this individual would benefit from further training in any of the subject areas listed. There should be a checkmark for each listed item.

	Needs Further Training	No Training Needed	Not Applicable/ Not Observed
1. Professional/Technical ability for this job	. . . .	. . . .	. . . .
2. Written communication	. . . .	. . . .	. . . .
3. Oral communication	. . . .	. . . .	. . . .
4. Analytical skills	. . . .	. . . .	. . . .
5. Leadership	. . . .	. . . .	. . . .
6. Relationships with others	. . . .	. . . .	. . . .
7. Planning and decision making	. . . .	. . . .	. . . .
8. Delegation	. . . .	. . . .	. . . .
9. Other	. . . .	. . . .	. . . .
_____	. . . .	. . . .	. . . .
_____	. . . .	. . . .	. . . .
_____	. . . .	. . . .	. . . .

Recommended Developmental Activities

For those items checked as "Needs Further Training" above, indicate specific developmental activities that you feel will strengthen this employee's performance in such areas. Consider not only training courses but also job rotation, special assignments, coaching, community service, etc.

Activity	Completion Date
_____	_____
_____	_____
_____	_____
_____	_____

_____   _____
Signature of Employee   Date

_____   _____
Signature of Appraiser   Date

_____   _____
Signature of Next Level Manager   Date

Comments — This space is provided for any additional comments the employee, appraising manager or others may wish to make.

_____

_____

_____

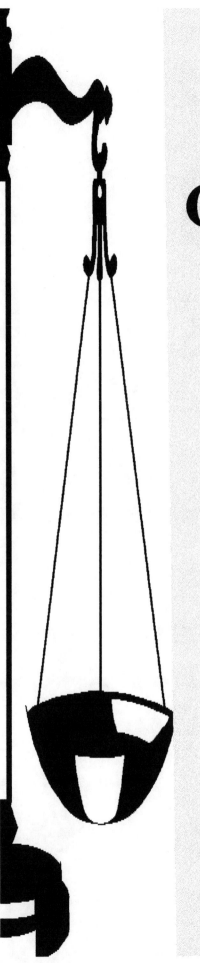

General Appraisal #7

NAME _____ TITLE _____

DEPARTMENT _____ DATE ASSIGNED TO PRESENT POSITION _____

DATE OF THIS REVIEW PERIOD: FROM: _____   TO: _____

INSTRUCTIONS:

This form is to be completed in the following instances:

- Annually

- Upon the Employee's changing from one job assignment to another.

- Upon the Rater's change in job assignment (which would result in a new Rater for the Employee).

- On an interim basis, as necessary, to review the Employee's performance.

- Should any of the above happen within three (3) months after completion of the previous PE/D Plan it will not be

  necessary to complete a new evaluation.

This evaluation covers all important aspects of the past performance of the employee, a summary of his/her current status, and a discussion of potential for growth and development. In addition, the report provides a vehicle for your personal discussion of the evaluation result with the employee.

OBJECTIVES AND EXPECTATIONS

Use measurable targets, numbers and dates to describe the objectives and expectations for the coming year. Consider this individual's sphere of influence as related to the following questions:

- What objectives and expectations do you have of this individual in meeting the goals of your business? *Be specific*

  as to financial and qualitative performance objectives.

- What is expected of this individual in terms of personnel management, nondiscriminatory practices, training and

  development of subordinates?

- What are the major personal objectives, including training and development objectives from the preceding Review

  period, which have been set for the individual?

PERFORMANCE LEVEL DESCRIPTION AND DEFINITION

Distinguished	Exceptional	Competent	Adequate	Unsatisfactory
Exceeds all objectives, actively develops teamwork and cooperation, seeks new and better ways to accomplish tasks, extremely capable and versatile in adjusting priorities to current needs, an effective communicator.	Consistently meets and often exceeds objectives. Actively contributes to achievements of overall company goals. Superior performance in all aspects of job. Performance well above the competent level.	Consistently meets and occasionally exceeds objectives, full utilization of ability and experience to produce the desired results that are expected from a qualified employee.	Usually meets objectives, areas for improvement noted in appraisal, level of performance is less than expected.	Doesn't meet objectives, falls short of required performance, consider probationary period, transfer to a more suitable job or termination.

Performance Results Against Objectives for Review Period

A. Continuing Responsibilities:

B. Objective	Weighting	Results Achieved	Measurement of Results (Timely, Quality, Cost Effectiveness, Quantity)	Summary of Results	
				Not Met	
				Not Fully Met	
				Fully Met	
				Exceeded	
				Significantly Exceeded	

PERFORMANCE EVALUATION

PERFORMANCE EVALUATION: Indicate by check marks how well this employee did on each factor that is relevant to the particular job. While comments are always appropriate, they should always be provided to explain instances where "Distinguished" or "Unsatisfactory" has been checked.

PERFORMANCE FACTOR	Distinguished	Exceptional	Competent	Adequate	Unsatisfactory	COMMENTS
Effectiveness in Planning and Organizing the Work: Consider how well the employee provides for both long and short range needs; how well he/she sets up work schedules; whether the individual approaches things systematically.						
Effectiveness in Assuring that Work Schedules are Met: Consider how adequately he/she monitors the progress of work; how well the employee meets deadlines without last minute rush.						
Effectiveness in Maintaining Required Quality: Consider the quality of his/her work; whether his/her quality standards are adequate; how well he/she sets up ways to assure meeting them.						
Degree of Technical Competence in His/Her Function: Consider how well the employee knows the requirements of his/her special field and how well he/she applies this knowledge; how well he/she stays abreast of new developments.						
Adherence to Company Policies and Practices: Consider the employee's knowledge about the company, its policies and procedures; how well the employee adheres to them, or inputs appropriate changes; ensures that safety procedures are followed.						
Initiative in Assuming and Discharging Responsibility: Consider the individual's willingness to assume new or additional responsibilities; how well does he/she follow through on assignments?						
Ability to Work Independently (Relative to Level and Position): Consider whether the employee coordinates his/her activities with others; is the employee productive when left alone?						
Effectiveness in Making Decisions: Consider the employee's ability to analyze the problem and make sound decisions.						
Ability to Accept Supervision: Consider the employee's willingness to perform as a team member including understanding the team's goals and accepting direction where appropriate.						
Effectiveness in Relations With Customers: Consider how responsive he/she is to customers within company guidelines and sound business practice.						
Effectiveness in Relations With Employees: Consider how the individual works with other employees; how well he/she gets their point across to others and gains their acceptance and cooperation.						
Managers & Supervisory Personnel Only — Management Skills: Consider the individual's ability to recruit, train and motivate within department and across company lines.						
EEO: Consider EEO efforts, consciousness & conduct						
Developing: Consider how well the manager coaches, develops, and promotes subordinates; how well manager appraises subordinates.						
Interpersonal: Consider how well the manager communicates up, down and across departmental lines.						

OVERALL PERFORMANCE SUMMARY: Indicate the performance level that most closely reflects how the employee's overall performance measured up to what should normally be expected from an employee with similar experience at this level.

Distinguished ☐   Exceptional ☐   Competent ☐   Adequate ☐   Unsatisfactory ☐

Professional Development Plan

1. Employee's Expressed Career Goals

   0-12 Months _____

   _____

   _____

   12-36 Months _____

   _____

   _____

2. Development Action Plan
   Describe the specific actions which you and this individual expect to take during the next review period to prepare him or her for increased responsibilities or management.

   ACTIVITY DESCRIPTION _____

   _____

   _____

   _____

   TARGET DATE _____

   I have read the above appraisal and wish to make the following comments

   _____

   _____

   _____

   _____

   Employee's Signature _____ Date _____

   Note: Signature of employee does not necessarily indicate concurrence with results of evaluation.

Salary Recommendation

Current Salary	$ _____	
Recommended Increase	$ _____ % _____	
Proposed Salary	$ _____	
Effective Date _____		
Next Review Date _____		

Reason for increase: Merit _____

Promotion _____

Adjustment _____

Promotion: New Position _____

New Level _____

Approvals

Reviewer	Reviewer's Superior	Human Resources

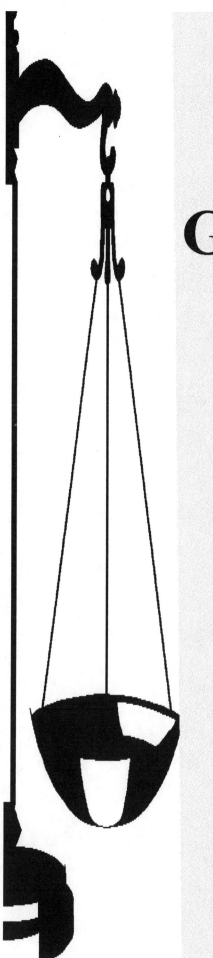

General Appraisal
#8

IMPACT REVIEW

☐ 90 DAYS   ☐ REGULAR

NAME _____   DATE _____

DEPARTMENT _____   PERIOD COVERED BY THIS REVIEW _____   ORIGINAL HIRE DATE _____

OVERALL PERFORMANCE RATING ☐ (N=NEEDS IMPROVEMENT, S=SATISFACTORY, E=EXCEPTIONAL)   (SEE PART I FOR DEFINITIONS)

PART I - JOB PERFORMANCE

Considering only the period covered by this report and using the appraisal codes below, the appraiser will: (1) assign to each objective or responsiblity the rating which most accurately describes the associate's performance (objectives should coordinate with departmental objectives). If the associate has more than five objectives or responsibilities, an additional sheet may be attached. The signatures should be completed after the objectives/responsibilities have been determined. Please comment on all ratings. (2) Based on the individual ratings of all objectives or responsibilities and considering the developmental factors in Part 2, determine an overall performance rating and enter it in the space provided at the top of this page.

APPRAISAL CODES
1. Needs Improvement - the level of performance during this rating period did not fully meet the established standards of performance or expectations.
2. Satisfactory - The level of performance during this rating period met the established standards of performance or expectations.
3. Exceptional - The level of performance during this rating period consistently exceeded the established standards of performance or expectations.

1. OBJECTIVE OR RESPONSIBILITY: _____   RATING
   COMMENTS: _____   ☐

2. OBJECTIVE OR RESPONSIBILITY: _____   RATING
   COMMENTS: _____   ☐

3. OBJECTIVE OR RESPONSIBILITY: _____   RATING
   COMMENTS: _____   ☐

4. OBJECTIVE OR RESPONSIBILITY: _____   RATING
   COMMENTS: _____   ☐

5. OBJECTIVE OR RESPONSIBILITY: _____   RATING
   COMMENTS: _____   ☐

COMPLETED BY: _____   _____
                     ASSOCIATE/DATE   PRIMARY APPRAISER/DATE

November, 1994

PART 2 - DEVELOPMENTAL FACTORS

This section is comprised of factors which directly affect how well an associate does their job, and should be considered in determining an overall rating of performance. Check SATISFACTORY, NEEDS IMPROVEMENT, EXCEPTIONAL, OR NO APPLICABLE (item #'s 11 & 12 only) for all factors. Comments are encouraged on any factor, however, they are **required** on those evaluated as NEEDS IMPROVEMENT.

	NEEDS IMPROVEMENT	SATISFACTORY	EXCEPTIONAL	N/A
1. Job Knowledge/Skills: Extent to which the associate knows the what, how and why of the position's requirements.	☐	☐	☐	
2. Dependability: Adheres to work schedules and completes assignments on time.	☐	☐	☐	
3. Interpersonal Relationships: Relates in a positive and professional manner with co-workers throughout the Company.	☐	☐	☐	
4. Communication: Openly exchanges information in a timely manner, knows who to keep informed, listens, understands, uses confidential information with discretion, writes and speaks in a clear, concise manner.	☐	☐	☐	
5. Initiative: Takes independent action appropriate to their job.	☐	☐	☐	
6. Time Management: Organizes work well and uses time effectively.	☐	☐	☐	
7. Problem Solving/Decision Making: Produces creative, innovative and workable solutions.	☐	☐	☐	
8. Teamwork: Ability to function in a joint cooperative manner while supporting the Company and departmental plans, programs, policies, procedures and other team members.	☐	☐	☐	
9. Quality and Quantity of Work: Maintains a high standard of work while increasing productivity.	☐	☐	☐	
10. Safety and Housekeeping: Keeps work area clean and hazard free.	☐	☐	☐	
11. Management Principles: Plans, organizes, delegates, coordinates and controls effectively.	☐	☐	☐	☐
12. Development/Evaluation of Associates: Maximizes associates' abilities and potentials through encouragement, empowerment, and a motivating environment.	☐	☐	☐	☐
13. Equal Employment Opportunities: Takes affirmative action in employment, development and advancement of protected classes.	☐	☐	☐	
14. Customer Focus Overall attitude of doing whatever it takes to make each customer contact (the next person in the process) prompt, accurate and enthusiastic.	☐	☐	☐	

Comments:

PART 3 - ASSOCIATE SELF-ASSESSMENT, PERSONAL IMRPOVEMENT AND CAREER INTEREST

IMPORTANT!! Part 3 is to be completed by the associate being evaluated PRIOR to the appraisal interview. The appraiser should provide the associate with a copy of the appraisal form at least two weeks before the scheduled date of the interview. It should be reviewed jointly by the associate and the appraiser during the interview.

SELF-ASSESSMENT: *Please comment on your performance during the period covered by this report. Particular emphasis should be given to any circumstances which affected your performance either positively or adversely.*

PERSONAL IMPROVEMENT: *What do you plan to do during the next appraisal period to improve your performance? How, in your opinion, can your appraiser and/or the Company help you improve?*

CAREER INTEREST: *Do you have an interest in other areas of the Company? Comment on specific jobs in which you may like to work, or any other career interest/desire not covered in appraisal.*

PART 4 - DEVELOPMENTAL SUMMARY

Based on the overall performance rating, the developmental needs as identified in Part 2, and the associate's comments from Part 3, the appraiser and associate are to complete the developmental action plan below. Primary focus should be on improving the associate's performance on their present job. Secondary emphasis should be place on preparation for possible future assignments.

DEVELOPMENT ACTION PLAN: *What specific actions will be taken by the appraiser and/or the associate to improve the associate's performance? What actions, if any, are recommended to prepare this associate for possible future assignments? Indicate who will initiate the action and when it will take place.*

PART 5 - POST-REVIEW COMMENTS
(to be completed and returned within 10 days of the review meeting)

TO BE COMPLETED BY THE ASSOCIATE AFTER THE IMPACT REVIEW MEETING:

TO BE COMPLETED BY THE APPRAISER AFTER THE IMPACT REVIEW MEETING:

Note: Signature does not indicate agreement/disagreement.

Associate's Signature _____ *Date* _____

Appraiser's Signature _____ *Date* _____

PART 6 - SECONDARY APPRAISER'S COMMENTS

The appraiser will share this with the secondary appraiser.

Signature _____ **Date** _____

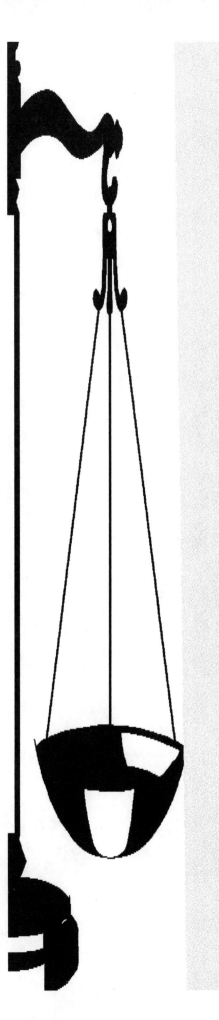

IV.

Participative Performance Appraisals

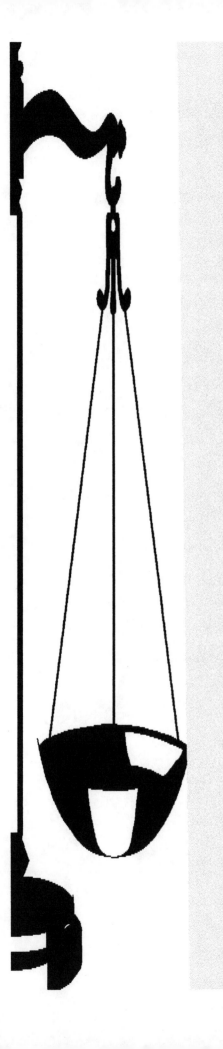

Participative Appraisal #1

MEMBER PERFORMANCE PLAN

Member Name	Member Number
Department	Location
Current Position/Title	Review Period

PURPOSE: The Member Performance Plan is used to communicate performance standards, to implement the Member's compensation program and as a guide for Member development and career planning.

USING THE FORM

The Member Performance Plan Form has been designed to lead you smoothly through the process step by step. Carefully read the instructions at the beginning of each section, which indicate the Member and Supervisor roles in the performance plan and when the steps are to be completed. The Supervisor's areas of completion are shaded for ease in distinguishing the roles.

Section I Instructions: *Member:* **At the beginning of the review period**, *describe up to five (5) goals/expected results that you will achieve in the next review period (Pages 1 - 2, A - E). Prioritize those goals/expected results as to their importance to your job, using a scale of 1-Low to 5-High. Write the organization's or Supervisor's goal to which your goals/expected results support in the Related Goal area.* **At the end of the review period**, *complete the Results Achieved portion.* **Supervisor:** *(Shaded Areas)* **At the end of the review period** *complete the Supervisor's Summary Statement and assign a Rating for the review period.*

SECTION I: GOALS/EXPECTED RESULTS	A	Prioritize the goals/expected results in terms of their importance to the job being performed (1-5)	Priority (1 Low - 5 High)

Related Goal (Organization's or Supervisor's Goal):

Goals/Expected Results:	Results Achieved:

Supervisor's Summary Statement:

Rating:	Exceeds Performance Requirements	Meets Performance Requirements	Does Not Meet Performance Requirements

SECTION I: GOALS/EXPECTED RESULTS	B	Prioritize the goals/expected results in terms of their importance to the job being performed (1-5)	Priority (1 Low - 5 High)

Related Goal (Organization's or Supervisor's Goal):

Goals/Expected Results:	Results Achieved:

Supervisor's Summary Statement:

Rating:	Exceeds Performance Requirements	Meets Performance Requirements	Does Not Meet Performance Requirements

SECTION I: GOALS/EXPECTED RESULTS	C	Prioritize the goals/expected results in terms of their importance to the job being performed (1-5)	Priority (1 Low - 5 High)

Related Goal (Organization's or Supervisor's Goal):

Goals/Expected Results:

Results Achieved:

Supervisor's Summary Statement:

Rating:		Exceeds Performance Requirements		Meets Performance Requirements		Does Not Meet Performance Requirements

SECTION I: GOALS/EXPECTED RESULTS	D	Prioritize the goals/expected results in terms of their importance to the job being performed (1-5)	Priority (1 Low - 5 High)

Related Goal (Organization's or Supervisor's Goal):

Goals/Expected Results:

Results Achieved:

Supervisor's Summary Statement:

Rating:		Exceeds Performance Requirements		Meets Performance Requirements		Does Not Meet Performance Requirements

SECTION I: GOALS/EXPECTED RESULTS	E	Prioritize the goals/expected results in terms of their importance to the job being performed (1-5)	Priority (1 Low - 5 High)

Related Goal (Organization's or Supervisor's Goal):

Goals/Expected Results:

Results Achieved:

Supervisor's Summary Statement:

Rating:		Exceeds Performance Requirements		Meets Performance Requirements		Does Not Meet Performance Requirements

Section II Instructions: By prioritizing your job skills, you are identifying one or two skill areas that need special attention because of your job assignment or your personal development. All skills are important! *Member: Prioritize the skill in the Member Priority area as (C) Critical, (VI) Very Important, or (I) Important. Two skills should be prioritized as (C), two as (VI) and two as (I). Reach concensus with your supervisor on the priority rating.* **Supervisor:** *(Shaded Areas) Prioritize the skill as (C), (VI) or (I) (described above) in the Supervisor Box, then reach consensus with the Member on the priority rating.* **At the end of the review period,** *complete the Supervisors Summary, and place an "X" in the appropriate rating, and a checkmark if there is a development need. (There may be a development need, even though the rating may be Outstanding).*

SECTION II: JOB SKILL (Describes HOW You Achieve Results)

LEAD, MANAGE AND MEASURE. Clearly assumes or assigns responsibility and authority for task and decisions; establishes clear objectives and measures for self and others; monitors process, progress and results appropriately; delivers timely and objective feedback. Gets involved and works with peers, subordinates and superiors as appropriate; contributes to the objectives of other Members or functions.

Supervisor's Summary Statement:			Member Priority (C) (VI) (I)	Supervisor Priority (C) (VI) (I)	Consensus Priority (C) (VI) (I)
Rating:	Outstanding Development Need ___	Commendable Development Need ___	Meets Expectations Development Need ___	Does Not Meet Expectations Development Need ___	

ORGANIZATION AND TIME MANAGEMENT SKILLS. Can effectively organize Members, materials and support to get things done; can handle multiple activities at once to accomplish a goal; uses resources effectively and efficiently; arranges information and files in a useful manner; manages time efficiently to achieve results.

Supervisor's Summary Statement:			Member Priority (C) (VI) (I)	Supervisor Priority (C) (VI) (I)	Consensus Priority (C) (VI) (I)
Rating:	Outstanding Development Need ___	Commendable Development Need ___	Meets Expectations Development Need ___	Does Not Meet Expectations Development Need ___	

INITIATIVE/CREATIVITY. Comes up with ideas to improve methods, products or cost improvements; open to ideas and suggestions to others; has good insight about which ideas and suggestions will work; good at brainstorming.

Supervisor's Summary Statement:			Member Priority (C) (VI) (I)	Supervisor Priority (C) (VI) (I)	Consensus Priority (C) (VI) (I)
Rating:	Outstanding Development Need ___	Commendable Development Need ___	Meets Expectations Development Need ___	Does Not Meet Expectations Development Need ___	

ANALYTICAL/PROBLEM-SOLVING SKILLS. Solves difficult problems with effective solutions by asking good questions; looks beyond the obvious and doesn't stop at the first answer; can see beyond underlying or hidden problems and patterns.

Supervisor's Summary Statement:			Member Priority (C) (VI) (I)	Supervisor Priority (C) (VI) (I)	Consensus Priority (C) (VI) (I)
Rating:	Outstanding Development Need ___	Commendable Development Need ___	Meets Expectations Development Need ___	Does Not Meet Expectations Development Need ___	

INTERPERSONAL SKILLS. Relates well with all kinds of Members; builds appropriate rapport; listens; builds constructive and effective relationships; uses diplomacy and tact; solicits feedback that encourages contrary views and to receive first-hand information, resulting in two-way communication; functions well as a team Member.

Supervisor's Summary Statement:			Member Priority (C) (VI) (I)	Supervisor Priority (C) (VI) (I)	Consensus Priority (C) (VI) (I)
Rating:	Outstanding Development Need ___	Commendable Development Need ___	Meets Expectations Development Need ___	Does Not Meet Expectations Development Need ___	

FUNCTIONAL/TECHNICAL SKILLS. Has the functional and technical knowledge and skills to do the job at a high level of accomplishment.

Supervisor's Summary Statement:			Member Priority (C) (VI) (I)	Supervisor Priority (C) (VI) (I)	Consensus Priority (C) (VI) (I)
Rating:	Outstanding Development Need ___	Commendable Development Need ___	Meets Expectations Development Need ___	Does Not Meet Expectations Development Need ___	

SECTION III. PERFORMANCE OBJECTIVES AND AREAS FOR IMPROVEMENT.

SECTION IV: JOB-BASED DEVELOPMENT PLANS.

Development Objective	Action Plan	Responsibility	Date to Begin

SECTION V: PERFORMANCE PLANNING SIGNATURES

Member	Supervisor	Supervisor's Manager

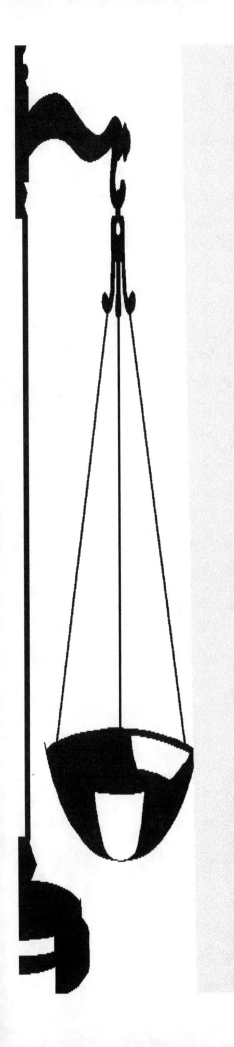

Participative Appraisal #2

EMPLOYEE PERFORMANCE EVALUATION

NAME		POSITION TITLE	
HIRE DATE	SOCIAL SECURITY NO.	LOCATION/DEPARTMENT	
EMPLOYMENT STATUS	LAST REVIEW DATE	IMMEDIATE SUPERVISOR	
DATE:	TYPE OF REVIEW: ☐ ANNUAL	☐ MID-YEAR ☐ PROBATIONARY	☐ OTHER

Instruction for Evaluators

Performance evaluations are conducted by the employee's immediate supervisor at least once every 12-month period or as needed. The goal is to reach a mutual understanding of the standards of performance expected, and an overall performance rating. As the information recorded on this form will become part of the employee's personnel record, and may be used in decisions concerning advancement, future training needs, performance-related salary adjustments or even disciplinary actions, take time to think through and complete all sections.

The performance evaluation process has been divided into two parts - one for the supervisor and one for the employee. Upon receipt of this package, give the employee the self-evaluation form to complete and at the same time schedule a performance meeting within two weeks. Then complete the supervisor's section which has been divided into two sections: Major Job Elements and Performance Factors.

First, list and briefly describe the major elements (duties and responsibilities) of this employee's position. Then, rate this employee's performance of these major job elements and indicate with comments your justification for each rating. YOU MUST MAKE A COMMENT WHENEVER YOU CHOOSE THE RATING "EXCEEDS EXPECTATIONS" OR "FAR BELOW EXPECTATIONS/UNSATISFACTORY". Next, rate this employee's performance on the performance factors listed, again you must justify a high or low grade. Note: you may give a half grade if you feel the performance is between two rating levels. Finally, give an overall rating for this employee's performance and sign the form.

After the review, please make two copies of the performance evaluation; one for your records, the other should be given to the employee. Return the original forms to the Human Resources Department.

NAME_____ REVIEW DATE_____

1. List the two, three or four major duties or responsibilities in your job.

2. Do you think your job description accurately describes your job?

3. What do you believe your job should be, and what duties and responsibilities should you have (or should not have) to make you more effective?

4. Describe your major performance accomplishments in the last year.

5. What have been your major disappointments with your performance in the last year?

6. What could you, your supervisor and/or the company do differently to help you better perform your job?

7. What are the personal development areas in which you most need to improve?

8. What other comments or suggestions should be addressed in this review?

STANDARDS OF PERFORMANCE

Evaluate the employee's performance since the last appraisal. Place an "X" in the category which best describes the performance level for the factor being rated. Include supporting evidence for each factor. YOU MUST MAKE A COMMENT WHENEVER A GRADE OF "4" OR "1" IS CHOSEN.

4 - EXCEEDS EXPECTATIONS	3 - MEETS EXPECTATIONS	2 - BELOW EXPECTATIONS/ NEEDS IMPROVEMENT	1 - UNSATISFACTORY FAR BELOW EXPECTATIONS
Consistently achieves results superior to expectations.	Normally achieves expectations; occasionally exceeds requirements.	Work is below average, not of quality expected; requires improvements.	Unacceptable; considerable and immediate improvements are necessary.

I. MAJOR JOB ELEMENTS (See Job Description)	4 = Exceeds Expectations 2 = Below Expectations 3 = Meets Expectations 1 = Far Below Expectations/Unsatisfactory
RATING: (Place "X" in box for appropriate rating.)	

1. | 4 | 3 | 2 | 1

COMMENTS:

2. | 4 | 3 | 2 | 1

COMMENTS:

3. | 4 | 3 | 2 | 1

COMMENTS:

4. | 4 | 3 | 2 | 1

COMMENTS:

II. PERFORMANCE FACTORS	4 = Exceeds Expectations 2 = Below Expectations 3 = Meets Expectations 1 = Far Below Expectations/Unsatisfactory				

PROFESSIONALISM	COMMENTS	4	3	2	1
The display of appropriate attitude, actions and work attire for the position; maintenance of own work area; flexibility; commitment to professional growth. Responsibility for actions, amount of supervision required, a skill level that inspires respect and confidence.					

DEPENDABILITY/PUNCTUALITY	COMMENTS	4	3	2	1
The thoroughness demonstrated by the employee in following through on assignments and instructions in a reliable, trustworthy and timely manner. Overall attendance and adherence to work schedules, office hours.					

INTERPERSONAL SKILLS	COMMENTS	4	3	2	1
Ability to express ideas clearly, concisely and effectively both orally and in writing. Listens well, shares work related information, tolerant of others' work styles. Ability to work with others in an assertive and effective manner. The exercise of authority or the response to criticism in a tactful manner.					

JUDGEMENT/DECISION MAKING	COMMENTS	4	3	2	1
The ability to think logically and practically before making decisions. Use of independent thought, originality and reasoning. Ability to prioritize work and timely implementation of workable solutions to problem. The ability to handle confidential information.					

QUALITY OF WORK	COMMENTS	4	3	2	1
The value of work produced by the employee and the thoroughness, accuracy, neatness and acceptability of the work completed. Ability to work under pressure and learn from previous mistakes.					

INITIATIVE	COMMENTS	4	3	2	1
The demonstrated willingness to make significant contributions with little direction, voluntarily start projects, attempt non-routine jobs and tasks. Energy, enthusiasm and ingenuity. The exercise of judgement and independent actions within limits of authority. The degree to which the employee is self starting and proactive.					

OVERALL RATING

MAJOR JOB ELEMENTS

1.	4	3	2	1
2.	4	3	2	1
3.	4	3	2	1
4.	4	3	2	1

PERFORMANCE FACTORS

Professionalism	4	3	2	1
Dependability / Punctuality	4	3	2	1
Interpersonal Skills (Communication & Cooperation)	4	3	2	1
Judgement / Decision Making	4	3	2	1
Quality of Work	4	3	2	1
Initiative	4	3	2	1

OVERALL RATING	4	3	2	1

_____   _____
Supervisor's Signature   Date

_____   _____
Next Level Supervisor/Manager   Date

_____   _____
Employee's Signature   Date

Employee Comments:

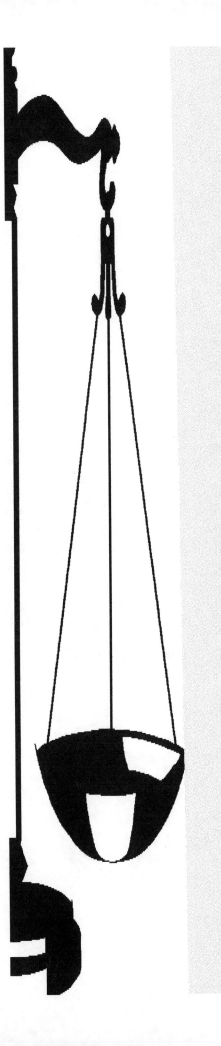

Participative
Appraisal #3

7. How has your supervisor helped you do a good job this past year?

    _____

    _____

    _____

8. Has your supervisor hindered your job performance this year? If so, please describe.

    _____

    _____

    _____

9. List some contributions you have made to your department's team:

    _____

    _____

    _____

10. In what areas did you further your education or training last year?

    _____

    _____

    _____

11. In what areas do you feel additional education, training/development would be beneficial?

    _____

    _____

    _____

EMPLOYEE SIGNATURE:_____DATE:_____

ANNUAL EMPLOYEE QUESTIONNAIRE

Name of Employee:_____Department:_____

Evaluation Period:_____Name of Supervisor:_____

1. What are your strengths as it applies to your current
    job?
    _____

    _____

    _____

2. What are some of the things you would like to improve or
    change within your department?
    _____

    _____

    _____

3. What are your goals for next year and what action will
    you take to accomplish these goals?
    _____

    _____

4. Suggest actions you would like your supervisor to take to
    help you accomplish your goals.
    _____

    _____

5. What skills do you have which you feel could be better
    utilized on the job?
    _____

    _____

6. How do you feel about your working relationship with your
    supervisor, i.e. communication, availability, etc.
    _____

    _____

Performance Evaluation

Employee Name _____ Job Title _____
Department/Co. _____ Supervisor _____
Date of Evaluation _____ Evaluation Period Based From _____ To _____

1. QUALITY OF WORK (Includes Accuracy): Ability of employee to provide quality work or product free of errors or waste. Consider carelessness, excessive hurry, inexperience, and/or need for training.

SUP EMP

☐ ☐ Product or work performance is of poor quality. Errors are frequent.
☐ ☐ Work is incomplete. Barely meets minimum standards. Requires frequent direction to improve quality. Recurrent errors.
☐ ☐ Work/product meets acceptable quality standards. Requires minimal direction. Usually accurate.
☐ ☐ Work is consistently of high quality. Requires very little supervisory direction.
☐ ☐ Consistently thorough in carrying out all details of job and error free. Final product nearly perfect.

COMMENTS: _____
_____
_____
_____

2. QUANTITY OF WORK: The amount of work performed relative to standards or known expectations. Consider effort, good use of time, and training.

SUP EMP

☐ ☐ Work output is inadequate to meet job requirements.
☐ ☐ Slow. Below average volume of work. Does just enough to get by.
☐ ☐ Volume of work is satisfactory. Output is sufficient to meet minimum job requirements.
☐ ☐ Very industrious. Does more than expected. Often exceeds deadlines or schedules.
☐ ☐ Regularly exceeds established standards of productivity. Consistently willing to do additional work. May accomplish special projects.

COMMENTS: _____
_____
_____
_____

3. CUSTOMER SERVICE: Is perceived by customers as dependable and responsive to customer requirements. Is able to get positive results in adverse situations. Consider level of courtesy and friendliness extended to the customer. Ability to maintain customer confidence and trust. Works cooperatively with other employees in meeting customer expectations/needs.

SUP EMP

☐ ☐ Blunt. Distant and aloof. Does not appear to care if others are satisfied. Rarely acts in ways which promote courtesy or service. Makes little effort to sustain favorable image. May arouse customer anger.
☐ ☐ Occasionally acts in ways to promote good service. Sometimes lacks follow through. Sometimes makes inappropriate comments.
☐ ☐ Promotes a favorable image and manages most customer interactions appropriately. Approachable. Responds promptly to customer inquiries. Readily assists customer to provide good service. Gives priority to satisfying others.
☐ ☐ Frequently exceeds job responsibilities to satisfy customers. Is cheerful and friendly.
☐ ☐ Inspires others to be courteous and very pleasant. Excellent at establishing goodwill. Exemplary customer service.

COMMENTS _____
_____
_____
_____

4. SAFETY: The degree to which an employee adheres to safety standards in the performance of their job and participates in safety related activities.

SUP EMP

- ☐ ☐ Disregard of safety policies/procedures. Often seen not wearing personal protective equipment and/or safe clothing. Does not utilize equipment safety guards. Accidents on the job. May appear generally uninterested in learning about safety.
- ☐ ☐ Work area is disorderly. Does not apply principles of accident prevention in daily work. Operates equipment without training.
- ☐ ☐ Familiar with safety responsibilities. Wears and maintains personal protective equipment. Reports hazardous conditions.
- ☐ ☐ Coordinates with other employees to reduce accidents. Applies good housekeeping techniques in work area.
- ☐ ☐ Observes all safety standards and participates in the Company's efforts to provide a safe work environment. May assist in training new employees. May serve on Company safety committee. Assures that tools are maintained and in good repair.

COMMENTS: _____
_____
_____
_____

5. JOB KNOWLEDGE AND VERSATILITY: The information concerning work duties that an individual should know in order to do their job. The extent to which an employee's skills and knowledge fulfill the responsibilities of the position. General knowledge of how their job fits into the Company as a whole and/or effects others in the department.

SUP EMP

- ☐ ☐ Inadequate knowledge of job duties. Does not apply knowledge/skills.
- ☐ ☐ Needs more knowledge of job to fulfill requirements. Requires frequent direction to apply knowledge/skills properly.
- ☐ ☐ Properly applies skills and knowledge of the techniques, procedures, products, and materials to perform job duties. Requires minimal supervisory assistance.
- ☐ ☐ Job knowledge and skill is above average. Understands all phases of job.
- ☐ ☐ Seeks additional job knowledge and skills and applies such to the overall improvement of the department/area. Has the ability and versatility to manage most circumstances.

COMMENTS: _____
_____
_____
_____

6. INITIATIVE: Ability to work independently. Consider ability to plan work and/or proceed with a job without being told each detail. Willingness to take responsibility for results. Desire to reach goals.

SUP EMP

- ☐ ☐ Rarely shows any initiative. Is not a self starter. Puts forth little effort to achieve goals.
- ☐ ☐ Requires some direction or prodding. Seldom performs other duties.
- ☐ ☐ A self starter. Carries out job responsibilities and makes suggestions for improvement in work methods. May help others.
- ☐ ☐ Is progressive. Does additional work without direction when necessary. Consistently sets higher goals than expected.
- ☐ ☐ High level of energy. Sets and achieves goals. Constantly strives for new methods.

COMMENTS _____
_____
_____
_____

7. ATTENDANCE: The record of work attendance. Consider excused and unexcused absence other than vacations and holidays.

SUP EMP

- ☐ ☐ Is excessively absent, tardy, or unavailable for work. Does not meet Company standards. Requires immediate improvement.
- ☐ ☐ Absence or tardiness is frequent.
- ☐ ☐ Regular attendance. Consistently on time.
- ☐ ☐ Seldom absent. Prompt. Notifications of absence are timely and to the correct person.
- ☐ ☐ Virtually perfect attendance and punctuality. Has achieved healthy balance between personal and work life so only absent in emergencies. Schedules vacations in advance with consideration of back up during absence.

COMMENTS _____
_____
_____

8. TEAMWORK: Considers the ability and willingness of the employee to work with others as a team member. Is perceived by customers and other employees as dependable and responsive to customer requirements. Consider level of courtesy, friendliness, and cooperation extended to others within the Company. Regularly supports the goals and objectives of the Company or work area.

SUP EMP

☐ ☐ Disruptive and antagonistic in working with others. Does not appear to care whether cooperation is extended or not. Chronically complains or criticizes. Acts independently without respect to how actions affect others.

☐ ☐ Usually gets along well with others. Occasional conflict with supervisor and/or personnel. Often allows "moods" to interfere with work and co-worker relationships. May have difficulty accepting constructive criticism. Sometimes makes inappropriate comments.

☐ ☐ Works effectively as a team member. Responds well to supervision and direction. Accepts constructive criticism.

☐ ☐ Works well with others. Cheerful and friendly. Consistently contributes when deadlines are critical. Represents company/department favorably. Actions compliment efforts of other employees.

☐ ☐ Exceptional team player whose contributions to the group are significant. Seeks constructive criticism and uses in a positive manner. Inspires others through behavior.

COMMENTS: _____
_____
_____
_____

9. FOLLOW THROUGH: The quality of assuming and fulfilling job assignments in accordance with directions given.

SUP EMP

☐ ☐ Frequently fails to follow directions. Requires constant supervision. Unreliable.

☐ ☐ Follows directions poorly. Requires some prompting to get the job done.

☐ ☐ Follows directions and requires minimal supervisory follow-up.

☐ ☐ Understands directions and conscientiously completes them. Always dependable.

☐ ☐ Consistently follows through on all assignments. Anticipates what needs to be done and sometimes proceeds without being asked. Meets highest level of expectations.

COMMENTS: _____
_____
_____
_____

10. PERSONAL APPEARANCE: The impression an individual makes on others. This considers cleanliness, grooming, neatness, and appropriateness of dress on the job, including safety factors.

SUP EMP

☐ ☐ Untidy. Overall appearance inappropriate for the job. Disregard for Company appearance policy.

☐ ☐ Sometimes untidy. Careless about personal appearance.

☐ ☐ Generally neat and clean; satisfactory personal appearance.

☐ ☐ Good personal appearance. Good taste in dress. Appropriate for the job.

☐ ☐ Unusually well groomed. Very neat. Excellent taste in dress.

COMMENTS _____
_____
_____
_____

11. COMPANY LOYALTY: Willingness to stand up for Company and promote its welfare. Willingness to put the Company ahead of immediate self interest. Identification with Company goals. Adherence to Company policies and procedures.

SUP EMP

☐ ☐ Openly critical of Company goals and objectives. Does not follow Company policy and/or standard procedure.

☐ ☐ Has little or no concern for the Company goals and objectives. At times does not follow Company policy and/or standard procedure and has subsequent negative effects.

☐ ☐ Is interested and supportive of the Company philosophy, goals, and adheres to Company policy.

☐ ☐ Works well with supervisor and members of the management team to accomplish goals and objectives of the department and organization as a whole.

☐ ☐ Enthusiastic behaviors. Offers helpful input when asked for suggestions for improved policies and procedures.

☐ ☐ Is an active participant in departmental planning and development of goals.

COMMENTS _____
_____
_____
_____

12. **JUDGMENT:** Extent to which sound decisions are made in routine work as well as in difficult situations.

SUP   **EMP**

☐   ☐   Makes decisions without basis. Neglects to take appropriate action. Does not make use of available information. Does not use common sense on the job.

☐   ☐   Occasional inability to make sound decisions. Sometimes makes hasty decisions without using available information. Sometimes fails to seek assistance.

☐   ☐   Generally demonstrates logical thinking by making sound decisions after considering available facts.

☐   ☐   Sound judgment and common sense exercised. Often makes appropriate recommendations for solution of problems. Adequate decisions in almost all situations.

☐   ☐   Displays exceptional ability to analyze and deal with a variety of situations that otherwise could be potential problems.

COMMENTS: _____
_____
_____
_____

SPECIFIC JOB RESPONSIBILITIES / STANDARDS

1. _____
_____

☐ Needs Improvement   ☐ Progressing Satisfactorily   ☐ Competent   ☐ Exceeds Expectations

Explanation: _____
_____

2. _____
_____

☐ Needs Improvement   ☐ Progressing Satisfactorily   ☐ Competent   ☐ Exceeds Expectations

Explanation: _____
_____

3. _____
_____

☐ Needs Improvement   ☐ Progressing Satisfactorily   ☐ Competent   ☐ Exceeds Expectations

Explanation: _____
_____

EMPLOYEE DEVELOPMENT
(Use separate sheet if desired)

A. Follow-up development plans from previous evaluation. Indicate performance area and progress towards inprovememt.
_____
_____
_____

B. Identify any areas of performance where improvement will enhance job effectiveness. Indicate performance area and plan for improvement. _____
_____
_____
_____
_____

Employee comments: _____
_____

Supervisor comments: _____
_____

_____   _____
Employee Signature   Date   Supervisor Signature   Date

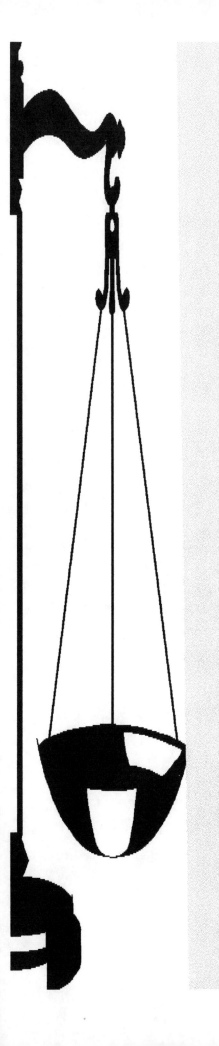

Participative Appraisal #4

Form 1
Employee's Self Assessment

Employee Name: _____   Department: _____

Employee Title: _____   Manager Name: _____

Employee SSN: _____   Period Covered: _____

Accomplishments (Describe your accomplishments in the past year against mutually understood goals and objectives for the position.)

Growth (Describe the key competencies and performance factors you have developed, especially in the past year, to make yourself a more valuable and versatile member of the organization.)

Developmental Needs (Describe the key competencies and performance factors you feel you need to further develop.)

Career Interests (Indicate your career interests including the kind of assignment you would like next.)

Evaluator Worksheet

Employee Name: _____   Department: _____

Employee Title: _____   Manager Name: _____

Evaluator Name: _____   Period Covered: _____

Instructions: You have been selected by the employee named above and his/her manager to provide feedback regarding the employee's performance. Please evaluate the employee against each of the performance factors shown using the rating system below. Each manager collects four to eight evaluation forms from clients, peers and subordinates of the employee being rated. The manger then consolidates the data and provides the employee with feedback from all evaluations, including that of the manager. Since ratings may vary from evaluator to evaluator, it is imperative that you provide the manager with as much detail as possible supporting your rating. You should return this form to the employee's manager within one week of receipt to facilitate the review process. The individual Evaluator Worksheets are not shared with the employee, and are destroyed after the appraisal meeting and sign-off with the employee.

Outstanding (1) - Consistently demonstrates exceptional performance.
Excellent (2) - Meets all requirements and often demonstrates performance beyond expectations for the position.

Fully Successful (3) - Performance meets expectations for the position.
Needs Improvement (4) - Meets some, but not all, expectations for the position.

Unacceptable (5) - Performance is inadequate. Major improvement needed.
Not Rated (N/R) - Unable to provide input on this factor.

Factor   Rating   Details and Examples

Job Competency
Possesses a high level of skill, knowledge, and ability in assigned functional area. Is not intimidated by complexity and gets the job done. A subject matter expert.

_____   _____

Teamwork
Integrates own activities with larger group. Readily gives and receives help. Values contributions made by others.

_____   _____

Communications
Communicates effectively (written, oral, presentation) up, down, and across the organization. Listens well.

_____   _____

Ownership
Takes responsibility and holds oneself accountable. Has a sense of urgency. Meets commitments.

_____   _____

External Focus
Listens and responds to customer/client needs. Helps suppliers improve productivity Looks outside own area for best practices.

_____   _____

Evaluator Worksheet (cont.)

Factor	Rating	Details and Examples

Initiative
Anticipates what needs to be done and does it. Willing and able to take risks. Looks for ways to do things better.

Problem Solving
Analytical, creative thinker. Finds proper solution at lowest cost that meets short and long term commitments.

Process Focus
Understands how things fit together. Ensures smooth hand-offs. Looks at the overall system and how to improve it.

Time Consciousness
Uses time efficiently in planning, anticipating, and responding. Looks to do things faster/reduce cycle time.

Versatility
Openly pursues change. Is multi-skilled and able to apply knowledge/skills across broad spectrum.

Personal Leadership
Sets example for excellence. Influential, persuasive, stretches for higher levels of performance. Treats all people with respect and dignity.

Managerial/Supervisory Skills
Provides sound leadership. Communicates vision and goals. Available to/supportive of staff. Effectively develops people.

Integrity
Maintains the highest standards of business and personal ethics.

91

Form 2
Manager's Consolidated Performance Factor Summary

Employee Name: _____   Department: _____

Employee Title: _____   Manager Name: _____

Period Covered: _____

Instructions: This form represents the manager's consolidated version of performance feedback solicited from four to eight evaluators who are clients, peers, or subordinates of the employee. The evaluators are agreed to in advance by the employee and manager, and are asked to complete a form similar to this Form 2. The worksheets are returned directly to the manager, who then consolidates the data and incorporates data from his/her perspective. It is the manager's responsibility to reconcile any inconsistencies among the evaluations, and gather details from the worksheets to support the final rating for each factor. The individual Evaluator Worksheets are not shared with the employee, and are destroyed after the appraisal meeting and sign-off with the employee.

Outstanding (1) - Consistently demonstrates exceptional performance.
Excellent (2) - Meets all requirements and often demonstrates performance beyond expectations for the position.

Fully Successful (3) - Performance meets expectations for the position.
Needs Improvement (4) - Meets some, but not all, expectations for the position.

Unacceptable (5) - Performance is inadequate. Major improvement needed.

Factor	**Rating**	**Details and Examples**
Job Competency Possesses a high level of skill, knowledge, and ability in assigned functional area. Is not intimidated by complexity and gets the job done. A subject matter expert.	_____	_____ _____ _____
Teamwork Integrates own activities with larger group. Readily gives and receives help. Values contributions made by others.	_____	_____ _____ _____
Communications Communicates effectively (written, oral, presentation) up, down, and across the organization. Listens well.	_____	_____ _____ _____
Ownership Takes responsibility and holds oneself accountable. Has a sense of urgency. Meets commitments.	_____	_____ _____ _____
External Focus Listens and responds to customer/client needs. Helps suppliers improve productivity Looks outside own area for best practices.	_____	_____ _____ _____

Form 2
Manager's Consolidated Performance Factor Summary (cont.)

Factor	**Rating**	**Details and Examples**

Initiative
Anticipates what needs to be done and does it. Willing and able to take risks. Looks for ways to do things better.

Problem Solving
Analytical, creative thinker. Finds proper solution at lowest cost that meets short and long term commitments.

Process Focus
Understands how things fit together. Ensures smooth hand-offs. Looks at the overall system and how to improve it.

Time Consciousness
Uses time efficiently in planning, anticipating, and responding. Looks to do things faster/reduce cycle time.

Versatility
Openly pursues change. Is multi-skilled and able to apply knowledge/skills across broad spectrum.

Personal Leadership
Sets example for excellence. Influential, persuasive, stretches for higher levels of performance. Treats all people with respect and dignity.

Managerial/Supervisory Skills
Provides sound leadership. Communicates vision and goals. Available to/supportive of staff. Effectively develops people.

Integrity
Maintains the highest standards of business and personal ethics.

Form 3
Manager's Assessment

Employee Name: _____   Department: _____

Employee Title: _____   Manager Name: _____

Period Covered: _____

Accomplishments (Describe the employee's accomplishments in the past year against mutually understood goals and objectives for the position.)

Growth (Describe what the employee has done, especially in the past year, to become a more valuable and versatile member of the organization, i.e. greater depth and/or breadth of skills and knowledge.)

Development Needs (Describe the key competencies and performance factors the employee needs to further develop.)

Overall Rating *(check one)*

☐ **Outstanding (1)** - Consistently demonstrates exceptional performance.

☐ **Excellent (2)** - Meets all requirements and often demonstrates performance beyond expectations for the position.

☐ **Fully Successful (3)** - Performance meets expectations for the position.

☐ **Needs Improvement (4)** - Meets some, but not all, expectations for the position.

☐ **Unacceptable (5)** - Performance is inadequate. Major improvement needed. *A separate performance measurement/ improvement plan is required for all individuals in this category.*

Form 4
Action Plan and Comments

Employee Name: _____   Department: _____

Employee Title: _____   Manager Name: _____

Period Covered: _____

Action Plan to Address Growth and Development

Manager Comments on Employee Career Interests

Employee Comments

_____   _____   _____
Manager   Date   **Employee**   Date   **Reviewer**   Date

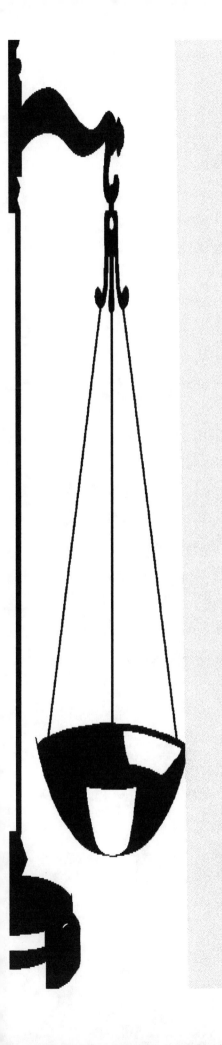

Participative Appraisal #5

SELF APPRAISAL FORM

Name _____

Supervisor's Name _____

Date _____

Circle appropriate answers, and comment below.

1. Do you understand all the requirements
    of your job? ....   Yes   Partly   No

2. Do you have regular opportunities to
    discuss your work, and objectives
    with your supervisor? ......   Yes   Partly   No

3. Would you like to have a formal
    meeting with your supervisor more
    than once a year?   Yes   No

4. Would you like to have more informal
    meetings with your supervisor more
    than you are currently having?   Yes   No

What parts of your job, do you:

a) do best? _____

_____

_____

b) do less well? _____

_____

_____

c) have difficulty with? _____

_____

_____

d) fail to enjoy? _____

_____

_____

4. Have you any skills, aptitudes, or knowledge not fully utilized
   in your job?_____

If so, what are they and how could they be used?

_____

_____

_____

5. Is there any special help or "coaching" you would like from your
   manager? Can you suggest ways of improving your working relationships with him/her, or others?

_____

_____

_____

6. Can you suggest training which would help to improve your
   performance or development?

_____

_____

_____

7. Wish List: During this year, I would like to achieve for
   myself and/or my department:

_____

_____

_____

_____

8. Additional remarks, notes, questions, or suggestions.

_____

_____

****

To ensure our records are correct, please note below your current
address and any other information Payroll or the Human
Resources/Safety Dept. should have.

Name: _____

Address: _____

_____

Phone Number: _____

Emergency Contact During The Day

Name: _____

Phone Number: _____

               _____

Please list any medical condition you have that we would need to
advice the Emergency Squad of should you be in an emergency situation
during the work day:

_____

_____

_____

PERFORMANCE APPRAISAL FORM
FIELD PERSONNEL

USING THE RATING AND WEIGHT SCALES BELOW, REVIEW THE EMPLOYEE'S PERFORMANCE IN EACH AREA AND NOTE AREAS WHERE THE EMPLOYEE EXCELS AND AREAS WHERE IMPROVEMENT IS NEEDED. GENERAL CRITERIA IN EACH AREA ARE LISTED. IF THE POSITION NECESSITATES ADDITIONAL CRITERIA, PLEASE LIST THE ADDITIONAL CRITERIA AND DISCUSS WITH THE EMPLOYEE.

RATING SCALE:

Each factor will be rated on a scale from 1 to 5. The evaluation is based upon qualitative and quantitative performance standards required to carry out the duties of your job.

1. UNSATISFACTORY - Performance falls substantially short of job requirements. Consequences may include, but are not limited to, reassignment, termination, corrective interview, demotion, or redefinition of duties. Monthly reviews will be held until the performance status changes.

2. MARGINAL - Performance does not consistently meet acceptable levels in <u>all</u> areas. Improvement is needed.

3. FULLY SATISFACTORY - Has performed at a fully satisfactory level, meets the requirements of the job in <u>all</u> respects and occasionally exceeds job performance standards.

4. DISTINCTIVE PERFORMANCE - Performance is significantly better than average. Performance consistently exceeds standards.

5. OUTSTANDING - Exceptional performance of unusually high caliber. Remarkable achievement and pacesetting performance.

WEIGHT SCALE:

Each factor will be weighted on a scale from A to C based upon your supervisor's view of its importance to the job you currently have with Heater.

A. A crucial part of the job responsibilities that the employee must concentrate much of his/her time and effort. It is of primary importance.

B. An important part of the job responsibilities. Must spend an adequate amount of time concentrating on it to ensure the job is performed effectively and efficiently.

C. A part of the job responsibilities, although not as critical as several other components. Should not be one of the employee's primary concerns, however, total neglect of it is unacceptable.

1. Job Skills and Knowledge:

Performance
Rating _____   Weight _____

* Demonstrates knowledge & understanding of job duties, equipment and appropriate work methods
* Applies knowledge and skills to produce quality work
* Completes assignments in a thorough and accurate manner
* Uses sound judgement when necessary to reassess projects/or situations
* Able to perform a wide variety of job-related tasks
* Integrates new subject matter into existing operations
* Completes necessary administrative paperwork

Comments: _____

---

2. Responsibility:

Performance
Rating _____   Weight _____

* Performs responsibilities as specified in the job description
* Maintains accurate inventory by assuring all material lists are distributed to proper personnel
* Utilizes company time wisely; shows a high level of work output on a daily basis with minimal supervision
* Routinely inspects & demonstrates knowledge of proper operation of assigned vehicle

Comments: _____

---

3. Customer Service

Performance
Rating _____   Weight _____

* Maintains courtesy and diplomacy with customers, and/or job contractors and other external contacts as well as internal contacts
* Makes self available to respond to customer needs
* Prevents unnecessary delays for customers
* When necessary, communicates appropriate information to the customer effectively and accurately
* Listens effectively

Comments: _____

4. **Housekeeping**

    * Routinely cleans, maintains and repairs his/her equipment and work area
    * Displays concern for company tools, equipment & materials
    * Keeps well lots and pump houses clean

    Performance
    Rating _____

    Weight _____

Comments: _____

5. **Problem Solving**

    * Demonstrates ability to clearly isolate and define problem areas
    * Formulates realistic solutions in a timely manner
    * Participates constructively in group problem solving
    * Presents problems, but offers solutions
    * Considers alternatives and consequences before making decisions

    Performance
    Rating _____

    Weight _____

Comments: _____

6. **Initiative**

    * Willing to assume new and challenging assignments
    * Expends the effort & time necessary to do the job well
    * Routinely shows an interest in improving his/her knowledge and skill level
    * When necessary, is able to work independently
    * Offers suggestions to solve problems or improve operations

    Performance
    Rating _____

    Weight _____

Comments: _____

7. **Organization**

    *   Adheres to priorities & deadlines; completes work within scheduled
        time frames
    *   Follows through on assignments despite setbacks
    *   Follows established schedules for work objectives for his/her areas of
        responsibility
    *   Shows a consistently low level of errors
    *   Produces neat, accurate, thorough and organized work
    *   Demonstrates flexibility in responding to priorities and organizational
        change

    Performance
    Rating _____

    Weight _____

Comments: _____

8. **Attendance & Punctuality**

    *   Reports to work as scheduled
    *   Follows call-in and approval procedures for time off
    *   Requests appropriate leave

    Performance
    Rating _____

    Weight _____

Comments: _____

9. **Interaction with Others**

    *   Expresses ideas and information accurately and understandably in
        both oral and written form
    *   Interacts and cooperates with others to ensure the Company's
        objectives and goals are met
    *   Resolves conflict effectively
    *   Shows interest in the job and in the Company
    *   Promotes departmental teamwork and interdepartmental teamwork
    *   Has a positive attitude towards his/her work
    *   Promotes respect, honesty, integrity, and fairness to all

    Performance
    Rating _____

    Weight _____

Comments: _____

10. Interaction with Supervisor

Performance
Rating _____

Weight _____

* Accepts supervision with a positive & appropriate attitude
* Receives constructive criticism well
* Communicates effectively with Supervisor
* If confused, requests clarification on policies and work assignments
* Executes direction and plans from Supervisor

Comments: _____

11. Organizational Development

Performance
Rating _____

Weight _____

* Promotes and actively participates in OD process
* Solicits ideas from other departments when appropriate
* Contributes to departmental & interdepartmental teamwork
* Supports Company objectives and mission statement

Comments: _____

12. Safety and Health

Performance
Rating _____

Weight _____

* Observes safety & health rules & regulations; works according to the standard procedures and practices
* Ensures that a safe work environment is maintained and that work areas are free from hazards
* Recognizes and reports any unsafe work practices and/or hazardous conditions to supervisor
* Is aware of location of material data sheets and refers to them when necessary
* Follows proper procedures on accident reporting

Comments: _____

LIST EMPLOYEE'S STRENGTHS _____

_____

_____

LIST AREAS IN WHICH EMPLOYEE COULD IMPROVE _____

_____

_____

If the employee needs to be put on an "Improvement Work Program", the employee, his/her supervisor, and personnel will create a program that allows the employee time to improve his/her overall performance level. At the end of the specified time limit, the employee and his/her supervisor will have a meeting to discuss employee's improvement.

EMPLOYEE: You must sign this form, thus acknowledging that you and your supervisor have discussed the results. Your signature, however, does not necessarily constitute agreement with the rating.

EMPLOYEE'S SIGNATURE _____

DATE _____

SUPERVISOR'S SIGNATURE _____

DATE _____

****

NOTES AND/OR COMMENTS   (By the employee and/or supervisor)

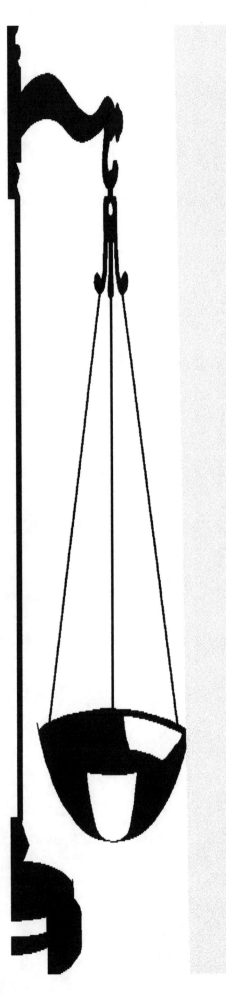

V.

Peer Performance Appraisals

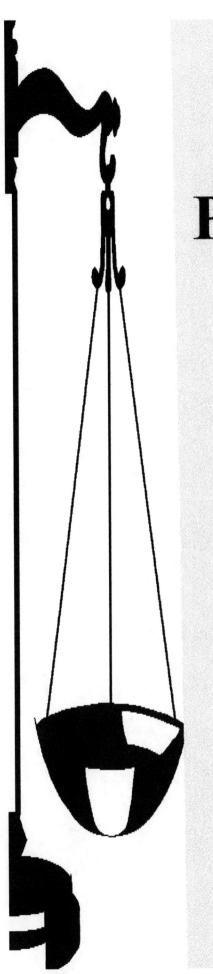

Peer Appraisal #1

DATE:_____

SUMMARY OF
PERFORMANCE IMPROVEMENT DISCUSSION INTERVIEWS

ASSOCIATE:	CO-WORKERS INTERVIEWED:
_____	_____
	_____

1. What specific services, support, reports, projects, etc. do you receive from or work on with this Associate? What is your overall level of satisfaction? What suggestions can you offer that would help him/her improve performance?

   General Comments:

2. What skills or knowledge, if improved, would help him/her become more effective in performing his/her job?

   General Comments:

3. Please identify any processes, systems and/or organizational issues that prevent/hinder him/her from doing his/her job.

   General Comments:

4. In addition to his/her usual responsibilities in the past year, what special project(s) has he/she worked on that required considerable additional effort? What specific contribution did he/she make to the project's success?

General Comments:

5. What suggestions would you have to improve the communication, either written or oral, between you and this Associate?

General Comments:

6. What are your observations as to his/her effectiveness in operating as a team member? What could he/she do to become more effective?

General Comments:

7. What are your observations as to his/her effectiveness in responding to customer problems, issues and/or complaints? What could he/she do to become more effective?

General Comments:

RATING YOUR PERFORMANCE:

Your Peers also rated your behavior as it pertained to the following questions. They were provided with the following performance definitions and checked the appropriate box. In addition, they were required to provide specific examples to support their rating, or it was deemed invalid.

Exceeds Requirements -- Associate's performance **consistently exceeds** what is required of him/her to complete assignments. His/her work product is usually error-free, detailed and clear. Deadlines are usually met before their due date, and Associate takes necessary action to avoid possible delays. Associate generally goes beyond what is expected in assisting other Associates and in providing and sharing information and offering solutions, thereby increasing communication, respect, harmony and teamwork within the organization.

Meets Requirements -- Associate's performance **consistently meets** the demands placed upon his/her position in terms of assisting other Associates and providing and sharing information. His/her work product is usually acceptable, but may occasionally require minor revisions. While his/her performance is steady, reliable and competent, prompting, guidance and/or direction may be required for Associate to produce what is required of him/her. Associate usually meets deadlines within his/her control, but if deadlines are missed, Associate willingly attempts to correct the problem to avoid delays in the future.

Below Requirements -- Associate's performance **does not meet** the demands placed upon his/her position. Work product is frequently unacceptable and/or requires major revisions, or output is below standard, causing delays in production. Associate appears reluctant to take action on his/her own without prompting, guidance or direction from other work groups. Deadlines within Associate's control are usually not met. Associate appears to make no effort to correct the problem to avoid future delays, or to provide or share information with other Associates.

The numbers following the questions indicate the number of Peers who rated your behavior accordingly:

	Number of Peers Selecting		
	Exceeds Req.	**Meets Req.**	**Below Req.**
1. The overall quality of Associate's work product that affects your job	_____	_____	_____

Comments:

| 2. Associate's overall timeliness in meeting deadlines that affect your job | _____ | _____ | _____ |

Comments:

| 3. Associate's overall ability and attempt to share relevant information with you that has a direct impact on your job | _____ | _____ | _____ |

Comments:

	Exceeds Req.	Meets Req.	Below Req.
4. Associate's overall dependability and reliability in following through on commitments to you	_____	_____	_____

Comments:

5. Associate's overall promptness in responding to your needs, questions and/or requests	_____	_____	_____

Comments:

6. Associate's overall promptness in responding to customer needs, questions and/or requests	_____	_____	_____

Comments:

7. Associate's overall friendliness and willingness to assist you with projects and/or meeting deadlines	_____	_____	_____

Comments:

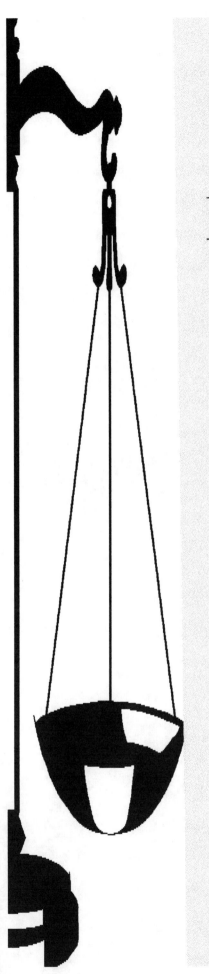

Peer Appraisal #2

PEER REVIEWS

* Supports our high performance work system

* Team members, enabler and manager meet offsite

* Team members evaluate each other on technical, safety, interpersonal, teamwork and leadership skills

* Scores are given (from 1-5) on above factors, and these scores determine the amount of their annual salary increase

* Customers (engineers, cross-over people) also give written input

* All verbal input given during the review is typed, and later given to the individual being evaluated

PERFORMANCE APPRAISAL FORM

Name	Employee Number	Salary Grade	Job Title	Review Period

JOB KNOWLEDGE

Performance Identifier: _____

Summary of Performance:

Development Opportunities:

SAFETY

Performance Identifier: _____

Summary of Performance:

Development Opportunities:

JOB SKILLS

Performance Identifier: _____

Summary of Performance:

Development Opportunities:

LEADERSHIP

Performance Identifier: _____

Summary of Performance:

Development Opportunities:

TEAMWORK

Summary of Performance:

Development Opportunities:

COMMUNICATION

Performance Identifier:

Summary of Performance:

Development Opportunities:

HIGHLIGHTS OF PERFORMANCE APPRAISAL REVIEW

OVERALL
PERFORMANCE
SCORE:

GOALS

My goals over the next review period (in "SMART" format):

SIGNATURES

This document has been discussed with me.
My signature does not signify agreement or
disagreement.

SUPERVISOR   DATE

_____

SIGNATURE OF EMPLOYEE   DATE   2ND LEVEL SUPERVISOR   DATE

CUSTOMER / PEER FEEDBACK FORM

CUSTOMER / PEER: _____   FEEDBACK PROVIDED BY: _____

DATE: _____

PURPOSE: The purpose of this form is to provide individuals with a simple communication tool for collecting feedback on actual performance vs. expectations.

This feedback form is intended to be a confidential method of gathering information to enhance overall performance or to develop specific skills within an area where development opportunities have been defined.

PROCESS: This form was designed to collect general and/or specific feedback.
The requestor has marked one or more of the following catagories for which they would like your open and honest feedback, and/or has written in specific questions at the bottom of this page.

CATAGORIES: _____ Job Knowledge   _____ Teamwork

                        _____ Job Skills   _____ Communication

                        _____ Quality   _____ Leadership

                                                   _____ Safety

SUPPLEMENTS: The reverse side of this page contains a brief list of "memory joggers." These are to be used to trigger thoughts within each defined catagory.

In addition, the "General Expectations - Process Operations" may be used as a baseline for measuring and reporting actual performance vs. expectations.

SPECIFIC AREAS FOR REVIEW / GENERAL FEEDBACK

1 _____

_____

2 _____

_____

3 _____

_____

4 _____

_____

5 _____

_____

6 _____

_____

7 _____

_____

_____

CUSTOMER / PEER FEEDBACK
"MEMORY JOGGERS"

Each of the following catagory lists "memory joggers." It is an abbreviated list of expectations to assist the customer/peer in giving feedback. The catagories are not all inclusive, they are listed for the purpose of getting the thinking process started.

JOB KNOWLEDGE

"Technical expertise specific to the job the person is operating (consideration of other jobs performed during the year should be taken into account.)"

1. Performance under abnormal or difficult situations.
2. Identifies and corrects problems. Helps others identify and correct problems.
3. Acquires and implements new information to improve knowledge of work area.
4. Is aware of his/her in-house customers' needs.

JOB SKILLS

"Person's general work skills package. Skills not specific to the persons unit op/ job description. Normally, those skills brought to GCI from previous experience, education or skills learned at GCI."

1. Utilizes technical skills and talents to enhance the teams level of productivity.
2. Works in an organized, effective manner.
3. Paperwork is complete, correct, and timely--meets deadlines.
4. Has a good attendance record. Arrives with ample crossover time prior to shift.
5. Practices good housekeeping and preventive maintenance in his/her work area.
6. Works ahead instead of getting things done "just in time." Makes the best use of his/her time to prepare their area for the upcoming shift change or process change.

QUALITY

1. Understands and demonstrates a high level of overall quality consciousness.
2. Does not attempt to isolate him/herself on quality issues. Eliminates quality errors through team participation.
3. Strives to understand his/her in-house customers' quality needs.

TEAMWORK

1. Promotes the team concept at GCI. (component teams)
2. Helps co-workers to attain their full potential.
3. Willingly helps others.
4. Participates in required team activities.

COMMUNICATION

1. Communicates openly, honestly, and respectively with all plant personnel.
2. Gives free expression of thoughts and ideas.
3. Handles conflict in a professional manner.
4. Receives and acts on feedback and/or criticism in a positive manner.

LEADERSHIP

1. Demonstrates team leadership abilities.
2. Takes pride in and promotes the peer-directed team concept.
3. Strives to improve work relations and remedy team conflicts.
4. Observes company principles and values.
5. Willingly shares and accepts responsibility.

SAFETY

1. Acknowledges and follows plant safety practices.
2. Takes the initiative to identify and correct safety hazards.
3. Uses safe work practices when operating equipment or handling hazardous materials.
4. Performs effectively in hazardous situations.

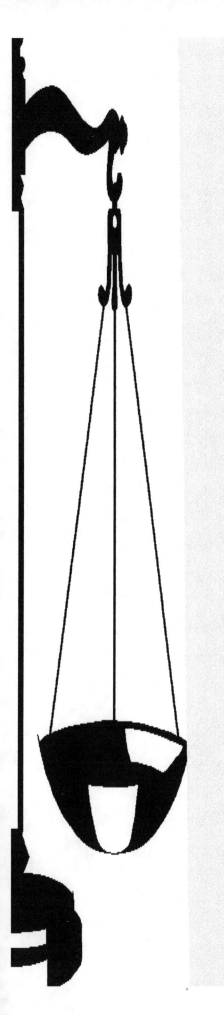

VI.

Team Performance Appraisals

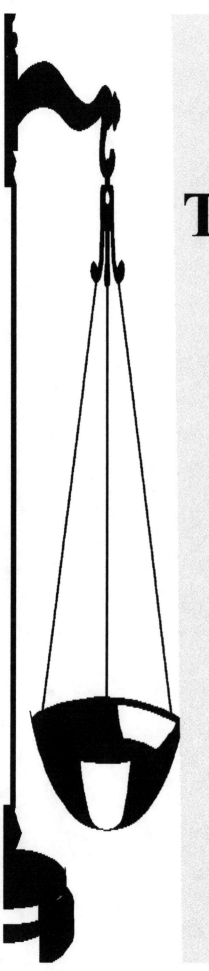

Team Appraisal #1

WORK GROUP SELF EVALUATION

EVALUATION CRITERIA	FAIR (1 pt)	GOOD (2 pts)	EXCELLENT (3 pts)
1. Meeting Frequency	Seldom	Semi-Regular	Regular
2. Meeting Mechanics (Agenda, Minutes, Action Assignments)	Sometimes	Usually	Always
3. Has Clear Work Group Mission/Purpose	Vague	Known	Formal
4. Clear Agreed Upon Work Group Goals	Sometimes	Usually	Always
5. Achieves Goals and Sets New Goals	Seldom	Sometimes	Regularly
6. Improves Work Processes	Seldom	Sometimes	Regularly
7. Uses Measurement and Appropriate Tools	Sometimes	Usually	Always
8. Acts as an Empowered Cohesive Team	Barely	Modest	Obvious
9. Has Visible Support and Feedback from Management	Minimal	Modest	Appropriate
10. Receives Recognition for Efforts and Successes	Minimal	Modest	Appropriate
OVERALL POINTS _____	10-17	10-24	25-30

WORK GROUP SELF EVALUATION

EVALUATION CRITERIA	FAIR (1 pt)	GOOD (2 pts)	EXCELLENT (3 pts)
1. Meeting Frequency	Seldom	Semi-Regular	Regular
2. Agenda Beforehand	Sometimes	Usually	Always
3. Assignments Given	Sometimes	Usually	Always
4. Minutes Issued	Sometimes	Usually	Always
5. Clear Agreed Upon Work Group Goals	Sometimes	Usually	Always
6. Regular Measurement	Sometimes	Usually	Always
7. Documented Improvements	Some	Modest	Significant
8. Management Visitation	1/year	2/year	>2/year
9. Acts as a Cohesive Team	Barely	Modest	Obvious
10. Uses Appropriate QIP Tools	Sometimes	Usually	Often
OVERALL POINTS _____	**10-17**	**10-24**	**25-30**

WORK GROUP SELF EVALUATION

Use this form after each Work Group meeting to assess the group's ability to work together productively. This form is most useful when discussed as a group and when working toward specific goals for Work Group functioning.

SKILLS	RATING	BEHAVIORS TO SUPPORT RATING
Preparing for the meeting	1 2 3 4 5	
Starting the meeting	1 2 3 4 5	
Inviting contributions	1 2 3 4 5	
Ensuring understanding	1 2 3 4 5	
Summarized ideas of others	1 2 3 4 5	
Keeping on topic	1 2 3 4 5	
Stopping competitive discussions	1 2 3 4 5	
Handling ramblers, know it alls, non-contributors	1 2 3 4 5	
Notes taken by all	1 2 3 4 5	
All contributed ideas	1 2 3 4 5	
Able to reach consensus on what the problem was	1 2 3 4 5	
Able to set a SMART goal	1 2 3 4 5	
All actively listened when one member was talking	1 2 3 4 5	
All were able to actually consider the others ideas	1 2 3 4 5	
All use assertive behavior to discuss divergent opinions	1 2 3 4 5	
Able to get "unstuck" when it seems that no one has any ideas	1 2 3 4 5	
Use resources available	1 2 3 4 5	
Make resources available	1 2 3 4 5	
Closing the meeting	1 2 3 4 5	
Follow up on the plans made after the meeting	1 2 3 4 5	

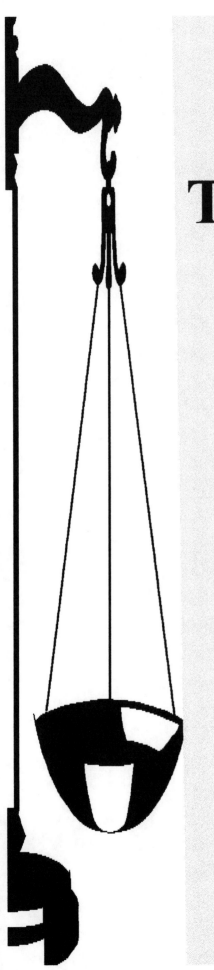

Team Appraisal #2

PERIODIC REVIEW

Evaluatee's Name:

Title:

Evaluator's Name:

Review Period Commenced: **January 1, 1995**
             Ended: **December 30, 1995**

The following discussion items constitute the basis of the individual's periodic review <u>during the period specified above</u>. Please review the standards of performance, personal objectives and strategies as they relate to each discussion item before responding. If necessary, please refer to the <u>"Periodic Review Discussion Guidelines"</u> (available in HR) for appropriate guidance in responding to the statements below.

****

1.   **Review the individual's job description and identify/discuss (generally and/or specifically) the work performed by the individual (e.g., tasks, projects, assignments, routines, etc.) during the review period. (Reserve discussions about major accomplishments for Item #3.)**

2. (a)   **Discuss any problem situations which may have made it difficult for the evaluatee to perform work assignments.**

(b)   Discuss any positive situations which may have made it easier to perform work assignments.

3.   Identify and discuss evaluatee's major accomplishments and/or achievements during the review period.

4. (a) Identify teams on which evaluatee is a contributor.

        1.
        2.
        3.
        4.

   (b) Discuss the individual's performance and contributions as a team player.

        <u>Team Comments</u>:

        <u>Facilitator Comments</u>:

5.   Identify and discuss the individual's contributions toward increasing the Company's customer base. (If this item does not apply to the evaluatee, please respond with N/A.)

6.   Discuss the individuals behavior and performance in the areas of customer relations and customer satisfaction, focusing on both external and internal customers.

7,   Discuss any areas where there may be opportunities or needs for future growth and development, (i.e., courses or seminars recommended by the evaluator)

8.   Discuss the individual's contributions toward the Company's objectives and strategies as set out in the Corporate Operational Plan. (If this item does not apply to evaluatee, please respond with N/A.)

9. (a)   General comments of the Evaluatee:

   (b)   General comments of the Evaluator:

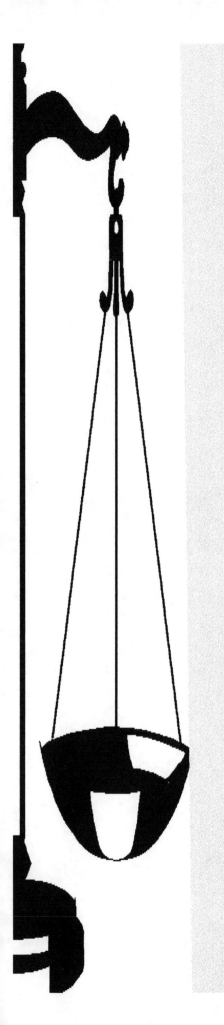

VII.

Upward
Performance
Appraisals

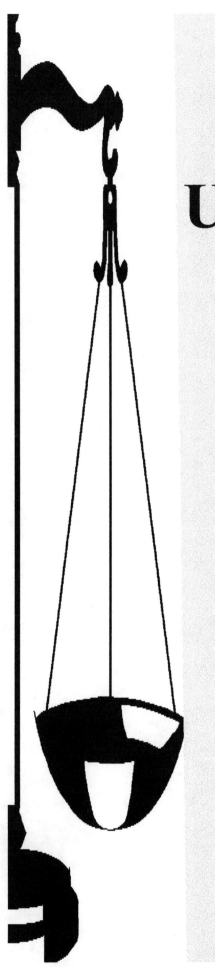

Upward Appraisal #1

SUPERVISOR APPRAISAL FORM

Supervisor's Name _____

Your Name (Optional) _____

Please review your supervisor's performance by indicating the appropriate letter.

P: Poor   F: Fair   G: Good   E: Excellent

1. Supervisor clearly states what he/she expects
    of an employee   _____

Comments: _____

_____

_____

2a. Supervisor delegates tasks to his/her employees   _____

Comments: _____

_____

2b. Supervisor allows employees the freedom to carry
    the tasks through   _____

Comments: _____

_____

3. Supervisor takes time out to listen to employee's
    suggestions or problems   _____

Comments: _____

_____

4. Supervisor displays a pleasant attitude toward
    his/her employees   _____

Comments: _____

_____

5. Supervisor provides all employees opportunities to grow
    and develop within their field(s) through:

a.) in house training (This relates to training directly
     provided by the supervisor to the employee)   _____

Comments: _____

_____

b.)   formal in house training (This relates to formal
      workshops held internally that employees could
      attend)   _____

Comments: _____

_____

c.)   outside training (schools, workshops, seminars,
      conferences, professional meetings, etc...)   _____

Comments: _____

_____

6.   Supervisor informs employees of administrative
      changes, policies, and procedures and sees that
      they are followed   _____

Comments: _____

_____

7.   Supervisor is able to unite his/her employees to obtain
      company objectives and goals   _____

Comments: _____

_____

8.   Supervisor is a motivator   _____

Comments: _____

_____

9.   Supervisor promotes an Organizational Development
      culture within department/unit   _____

Comments: _____

_____

10.   Supervisor handles disciplinary matters promptly and
      equitably with his/her employees   _____

Comments: _____

_____

11. Supervisor is supportive of his/her staff _____

Comments: _____

_____

12. Supervisor demonstrates leadership _____

Comments: _____

_____

13. Supervisor does not expect more of the employees than the supervisor is willing to put forth _____

Comments: _____

_____

OTHER COMMENTS

_____

_____

_____

_____

_____

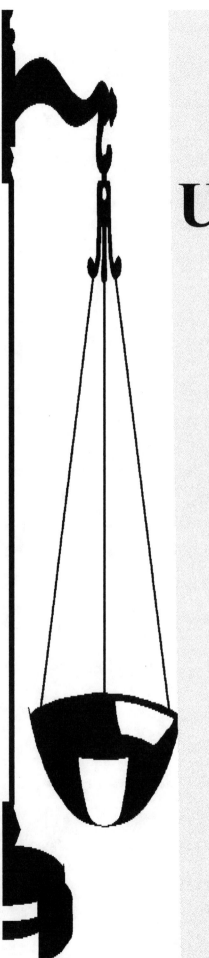

Upward Appraisal
#2

SUPERVISOR EVALUATION   SUPERVISOR NAME:

_____

For each of the following statements, indicate where your supervisor would place on a scale of 1 to 5.

	1 **Never** **Does** **This**	**2** **Might** **Do This** **Sometime**	**3** **Does** **About ½** **The Time**	**4** **Does** **Most Of** **The Time**	**5** **Always** **Does** **This**
Rating					

_____ 1. Supervisor is willing to listen to and try other's ideas.
_____ 2. Supervisor gives me adequate responsibility and authority to get things done.
_____ 3. Supervisor asks my opinion on how to accomplish work.
_____ 4. Supervisor is conscientious.
_____ 5. Supervisor lets me demonstrate my ability.
_____ 6. Gets along with employees they supervise.
_____ 7. Makes me feel a part of the team.
_____ 8. Encourages me to do the best job possible.
_____ 9. Is fair and equitable in most decisions.
_____10. Admits to making mistakes.
_____11. Appreciates my work and lets me know it.
_____12. Practices he/she preaches.
_____13. Is proud to work here and shows it.
_____14. Is dependable--you can count on the same decision consistently.
_____15. Respects me and my opinions.
_____16. Takes safety and accident prevention seriously.
_____17. Clearly explains what needs to be done.
_____18. Keeps me informed of things that affect me.

Your Comments:

_____

_____

_____

_____

_____

This evaluation form will only be review by me. Supervisors will only receive a compiled copy of all of their ratings. We are using this tool to try to identify how supervisors perform and to determine what type of training would be beneficial. You may complete the rating form and remain anonymous.

Thank you for your help and cooperation.

Managing Director   149

150

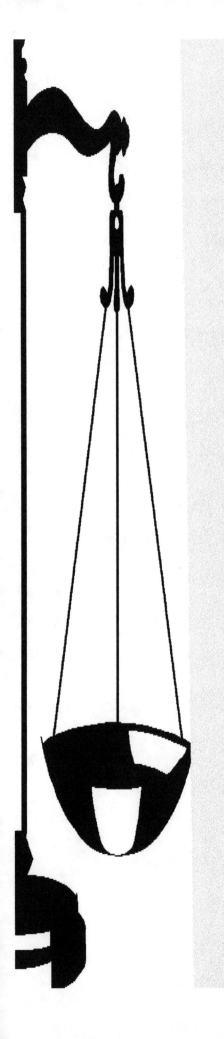

VIII.

Project/Task Appraisals

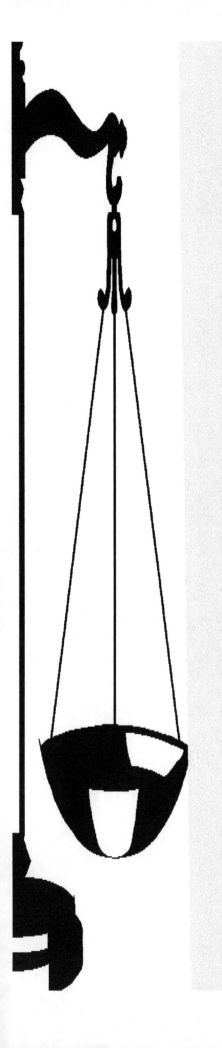

Project/Task
Appraisal #1

PROJECT/TASK PERFORMANCE REVIEW

Employee _____   Title _____
Supervisor _____   Date: _____
Project/Task Name duration: _____

The project/task review is to be completed at the end of a project assignment or when a Project Task of any duration has been completed. (Short assignments of one or a few days are not usually evaluated but outstandingly good or poor work should be documented even if it is only of short duration.) This evaluation is to be completed by the person who assigned and supervised the work (even if a lower grade level than the employee doing the work) remained with the employee and sent to the employee's administrative supervisor to be used as part of the annual performance evaluation.

If there was no opportunity for the employee to perform in one or more of the dimensions mark that one not applicable (N/A).

Please give one or more examples of exceeding expectations or needs improvement. **Note that the expectations should be for someone who has the background and experience to do the job (a competent employee). DO NOT use either yourself or some ideal person as the standard against which to evaluate the employee's performance.**

Performance Dimension	Exceeded Expectations	Met Expectations	Improvement Needed	N/A
Quality of Work				
Quantity of Work				
Client Relationship				
Writing Skill				
Presentation Skill				
Initiative				
Willingness to ask questions				
Problem Solving				
Application of Technical Knowledge				

#24988

155

Examples of Exceeding Expectations	Examples of what specifically needs improvement

Employee _____ Project/Task Supervisor _____ Date _____

Rev 1.0

#24988

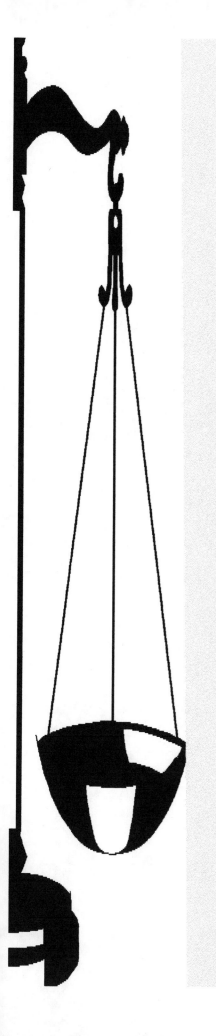

Project/Task Appraisal #2

Project Management Performance Review

Employee Name_____ Grade/Title_____

Supervisor Name_____ Review: ☐ Midyear ☐ Yearend

Review/Evaluation Period: From _____ To _____

At the beginning of the review period supervisor and employee meet to discuss performance expectations and objectives for the coming year.

Midyear Performance Review

The **midyear review** is expected to focus on results-to-date, what has been working well and what needs to be improved. The employee and supervisor complete the review form individually and then meet to discuss the employee's relative strengths on the performance dimensions. For this review the employee is the focus of comparison using the following scale. **The purpose of this review is feedback.**

1 An outstanding skill, consistently effective use of the behaviors required by the performance dimensions

2 A strength when compared to employee's skill level in other performance dimensions

3 Average ability when compared to employee's skill level in other dimensions

4 Not a strength when ability compared to performance on other dimensions

Up to three performance dimensions may be scored a 1; up to three performance dimensions may be scored a 2; the rest of the performance dimensions may be scored a 3 or 4.

Yearend Evaluation

The **yearend review** follows a similar process except that the employee's performance is compared with his or her peers performing similar functions. **The purpose of this review is feedback and to evaluate the employee.**

- Employee and supervisor individually prepare form

- Meeting to discuss results and any improvement needed

- Supervisor prepares final form, which may be revised because of meeting with employee. Form submitted for salary administration purposes and higher management approval

- Supervisor reviews final evaluation with employee and result of salary review

Yearend Rating Scale

A More effective performance than all but a few peers

B More effective performance than most peers

C Performance at the level of a majority of peers

D Performance at a lower level than most peers. Improvement is needed in more than one dimension

Performance Dimensions

Each performance dimension is rated based on the employee's performance for the year. The performance dimensions are not exclusively described by the phrases under them. There may be other specific skills, abilities or job performance considered when rating the dimension.

Client Relationship_____

- Establishes and maintains positive working relationship with clients.

- Keeps clients informed of project status.

- Anticipates and takes steps to solve client problems.

- Responsive to client requests.

Quality and Quantity_____

- Accurate, clear, thorough, organized work that meets or exceeds client expectations.

- Able to meet contract and M&E standards under normal conditions, as well as, when under pressure or changing conditions.

- Implements TAT and QA/QC on projects.

- Knows and appropriately applies M&E policies and procedures.

Planning and Scheduling_____

- Creates work plan appropriate to type of project, client, contract.

- Creates, monitors, updates and manages schedule.

- Consistently meets schedules.

- Identifies, accurately forecasts and obtains needed resources.

- Includes project team in planning and scheduling development and implementation.

Technical Competence_____

- Maintains technical expertise appropriate to job requirements.

- Work products show correct and often innovative application of technical knowledge.

- Ensures that project staff are trained and up-to-date.

- Able to provide technical guidance to project staff.

Communications_____

- Gathers and transmits information effectively.

- Oral and written communications are clear, concise and achieve intended objectives.

- Keeps appropriate documentation for project events and about staff performance.

- Establishes and maintains continuous, positive, cooperative communication with clients, project staff and others.

Business Development_____

- Makes effective contributions to pricing and go/no-go decisions.

- Develops strategies for, (and achieves), new orders from existing clients and orders from new clients.

- Develops capture strategies for proposals.

  Maintains contacts with existing and previous clients.

- Proactively seeks new ways to find and then maintain clients.

Cost Control/Cash Management_____

- Negotiates contract and payment terms and conditions, as favorable as possible, for M&E.

- Identifies and pursues opportunities to improve methods and procedures, to be more cost-effective.

- Obtains consensus with client early in project about invoicing process, format and requirements.

- Submits accurate, timely invoices.

- Follows up with client (15 days) to ensure invoice receipt and prompts resolution of any questions.

- Manages cash on projects to have favorable impact on region's DSO (days for billing/collection cycle).

- Obtains change orders in advance of performing work.

- Brings in projects at or under budget.

Problem Solving_____

- Recognizes potential problems and acts to prevent them.

- Correctly and innovatively applies expertise to solving technical problems.

- Enlists the aid of any appropriate source to solve problems.

- Treats client's problems with the same urgency as the client.

Leadership/Supervision_____

- Acts as a spokesperson for corporate/regional vision and goals.

- Adjusts direction and feedback according to individual/work-group needs.

- Delegates work to staff and helps develop staff capability to take on more, different, or new tasks.

- Observes, documents, gives positive and negative feedback and effectively reviews staff performance.

- Models teamwork and cooperative effort between functions, departments and regions. (Leads by example)

- Demonstrates support of principles of equal opportunity and affirmative action.

Interpersonal Skills_____

- Anticipates and prevents conflict when possible, otherwise is able to resolve conflicts so that performance/deliverable does not suffer.

- Acts in a way that gains respect and trust of staff, peers, managers, and clients.

- Willing to listen to and deal with the concerns of staff. Willing to listen to contrary opinions and not ignore them.

- Seeks to provide service to others regardless of position in the company.

- Does not participate in, nor allow, rumors or destructive communication about the personality or performance of others.

- Able to disagree with others without creating alienation or ill-will.

Each employee is expected to have one or more specific objectives. These objectives and measures may be carried forward from the previous year, set at the beginning of the review period, and added, changed or deleted during the review period as necessary. A supplementary sheet may be added if more space for objectives is needed.

Objectives are rated at midyear, year end and at completion of the objective

Objectives Rating Scale

E = Exceeded Target

M = Met Target

P(+) = In Progress, On Target

P(−) = In Progress, Off Target

D = Did not Meet

N/A = Not Applicable, No Progress Yet, New Objective

OBJECTIVE/MEASURE	Mid Year	Year End	At Completion
1.			

Supervisor Comments: _____

_____

_____

_____

Development plans for maintaining and improving work skills and for preparation
to take on more or different assignments.

_____

_____

_____

_____

_____

_____

_____

_____

_____

Performance Dimensions Evaluation Summary:

____Client Relationship   ____Communication   ____Quality and Quantity

____Business Development   ____Planning and Scheduling   ____Problem Solving

____Cash Management/Cost Control ____Leadership/Supervision   ____Technical Competence

____Interpersonal Skills

Objectives Evaluation Summary: (Keyed to the Objective Number from Inside Sheet)

1____   2____   3____   4____   5____   6____   7____   8____

Overall Evaluation: ☐ A   ☐ B   ☐ C   ☐ D*

(Yearend rating based on performance dimensions and objectives evaluations.)

*Improvement Plan Required to be completed and attached.

Supervisor Signature/Date _____ Reviewer Signature/Date_____

Reviewer Signature/Date _____ Employee Signature/Date_____

Employee Comments: _____

_____

_____

_____

_____

4352df

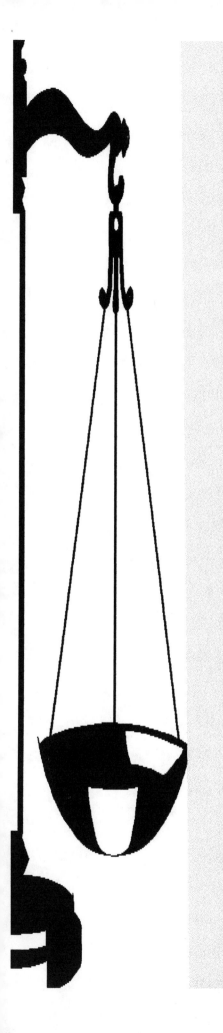

IX.

Executive/
Management
Appraisals

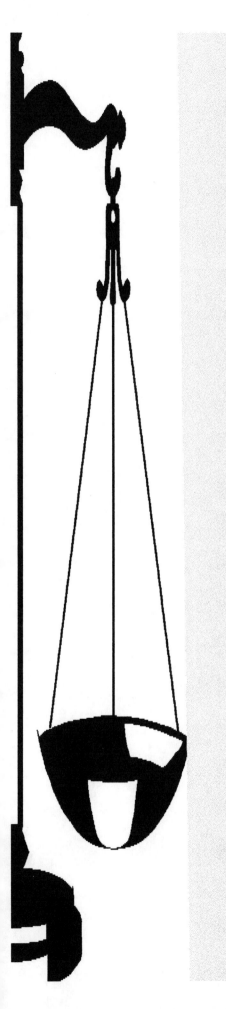

Executive/
Management #1

PERFORMANCE REVIEW
General Manager

To: Board Member - Please review the list of accomplishments submitted by the General Manager. For each functional area, list your overall evaluation. Use Board Policy A-4 as a guide to your decision. **When you check: Does Not Meet the Expectation or Exceeds the Expectation,** provide a brief explanation to support the evaluation.

1. Functional Area: PLANNING

☐ Exceeds the Expectation   ☐ Meets the Expectation   ☐ Does Not Meet the Expectation

Explanation: _____

_____

_____

_____

_____

2. Functional Area: ORGANIZATION

☐ Exceeds the Expectation   ☐ Meets the Expectation   ☐ Does Not Meet the Expectation

Explanation: _____

_____

_____

_____

_____

3. Functional Area: OPERATIONS

☐ Exceeds the Expectation ☐ Meets the Expectation ☐ Does Not Meet the Expectation

Explanation: _____

_____

_____

_____

_____

4. Functional Area: CONTROL

☐ Exceeds the Expectation ☐ Meets the Expectation ☐ Does Not Meet the Expectation

Explanation: _____

_____

_____

_____

_____

Other comments helpful to the General Manager: _____

_____

_____

_____

_____

_____

Signed: _____, Member   Date: _____

Board of Director

Please return this form to the Consultant to the Board of Directors

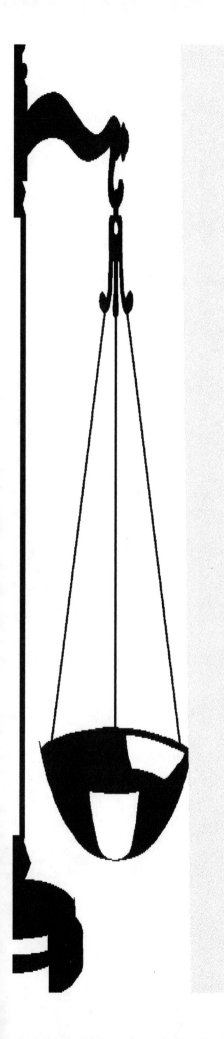

Executive/ Management #2

MANAGEMENT/EXECUTIVE EMPLOYEE
PERFORMANCE REVIEW

Employee Name	Position/Title	Employee Number	Date Of Hire

Department	Reviewing Manager	Date Of Last Review	Current Review Date	Next Scheduled Review Date

SECTION I : Describe the assignments and major responsibilities for the review period.

SECTION II : Goal and objective accomplishments: Indicate the actual performance relative to goals and write comments to explain the ratings.

Fails To Meet Standards	Needs Improvement To Meet Standards	Fully Meets Standards	Exceeds Standards	Far Exceeds Standards
1	2	3	4	5

Goal Or Objective	Performance Rating And Comments

General Comments Relating To Difficulty In Achieving Goals :

SECTION III : Indicate the performance level rating for each of the following key result areas or categories. Write comments to explain the ratings. If possible, include observations and dates of actual performance. NOTE: If a category does not apply, cross it out. Several examples of behavior are included under each key result area. These are not meant to be inclusive of all proper behaviors for that category.

Fails To Meet Standards	Needs Improvement To Meet Standards	Fully Meets Standards	Exceeds Standards	Far Exceeds Standards
1	2	3	4	5

PLANNING:

* Establishes both short and long term plans to meet future needs.

* Shows foresight in recognizing problems in areas of responsibility.

* Foresees changes and trends relevant to area of responsibility.

* Adheres to schedules and plans.

Comments :

Rating : [   ]

ADMINISTRATION:

* Gives attention to those areas of responsibility that are of an ongoing nature.

* Follows up on problems and decisions.

* Maintains controls over areas of accountability.

* Keeps own areas of responsibility, and all associated system and procedures, functioning smoothly over extended periods of time.

Comments :

Rating : [   ]

FINANCIAL:

* Tracks and adheres to financial plan.

* Makes sound decisions that consider cost/benefit.

* Accurately estimates expense levels, capital budgets, and other factors.

* Shows innovation in reducing expenses.

Comments :

Rating : [   ]

DECISION MAKING AND JUDGEMENT:

* Accumulates all relevant information prior to making job-related decidions.

* Presents well considered alternatives when making recommendations.

* Makes decisions in a timely manner.

* Notifies all affected parties prior to implementing decisions.

Comments :

Rating : [   ]

PERFORMANCE STANDARDS: * Communicates performance standards to employees. * Evaluates employees based on measurable behavior or results. * Puts time and effort into improving performance in assigned areas of responsibility. * Carries out in-depth analyses of department performance.	**Comments :** Rating : [ ]
INNOVATION AND CHANGE: * Initiates change when necessary. * Takes action quickly to correct or prevent problems. * Generates ideas and creative solutions. * Shows enthusiasm for new ideas, programs, and procedures.	**Comments :** Rating : [ ]
MANAGEMENT EFFECTIVENESS: * Delegates, then supervises performance. * Maintains composure under trying circumstances. * Utilizes personal time effectively. * Shows personal organization in filing and record keeping.	**Comments :** Rating : [ ]
KNOWLEDGE: * Demonstrates technical knowledge. * Displays knowledge and expertise of sound management practices. * Directs efforts towards personal improvement of job knowledge.	**Comments :** Rating : [ ]
EMPLOYEE RELATIONSHIPS AND DEVELOPMENT: * Selects competent employees. * Trains and develops employees. * Flexibly adjusts administrative techniques and styles when working with employees of different skills and abiliiities. * Gives positive or negative reinforcement promptly to improve employee's performance. * Periodically meets with employees to share information which will affect them.	**Comments :** Rating : [ ]

173

ORGANIZATIONAL RELATIONSHIPS:

* Executes directions and plans received from superiors and higher administrative units independent of personal likes/dislikes.

* Accepts criticism and feedback from management with minimum defensiveness.

* Demonstrates skill in communicating with others orally (for example, conducting meetings or speaking.)

* Provides information or help to superiors or peers when needed.

* Shows appropriate assertiveness in expressing and advocating points of view.

* Writes reports and memos which are clear and useful.

Comments :.

Rating : [   ]

Additional Comments and other review criteria not covered in previous sections:

SECTION IV: Future goals and performance improvement development plan.

SECTION V: Summary of overall rating. Please include summary of which areas most significantly affected the overall review:

Overall Rating : [   ]

Fails To Meet Standards	Needs Improvement To Meet Standards	Fully Meets Standards	Exceeds Standards	Far Exceeds Standards
1	2	3	4	5

Comments of Employee:			
Manager	**Date Submitted**	**Human Resources Department Signature**	**Date**
Next Level Management	**Date**	**Employee's Signature ***	**Date**

* Signature signifies receipt of appraisal only, and does not necessarily indicate agreement.

175

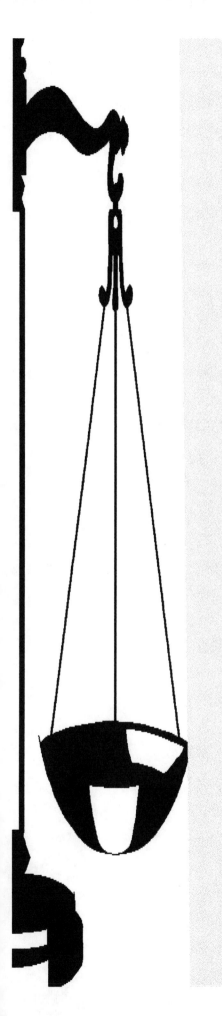

Executive/ Management #3

PERFORMANCE APPRAISAL FORM
SUPERVISORY AND MANAGEMENT PERSONNEL

USING THE RATING AND WEIGHT SCALES BELOW, REVIEW THE EMPLOYEE'S PERFORMANCE IN EACH AREA AND NOTE AREAS WHERE THE EMPLOYEE EXCELS AND AREAS WHERE IMPROVEMENT IS NEEDED. GENERAL CRITERIA IN EACH AREA ARE LISTED. IF THE POSITION NECESSITATES ADDITIONAL CRITERIA, PLEASE LIST THE ADDITIONAL CRITERIA AND DISCUSS WITH THE EMPLOYEE.

RATING SCALE:

Each factor will be rated on a scale from 1 to 5. The evaluation is based upon qualitative and quantitative performance standards required to carry out the duties of your job.

1. UNSATISFACTORY - Performance falls substantially short of job requirements. Consequences may include, but are not limited to, reassignment, termination, corrective interview, demotion, or redefinition of duties. Monthly will be held until the performance status changes.

2. MARGINAL - Performance does not meet an acceptable level in <u>all</u> areas. Improvement is needed.

3. FULLY SATISFACTORY - Has performed at a fully satisfactory level, meets the requirements of the job in <u>all</u> respects and occasionally exceeds job performance standards.

4. DISTINCTIVE PERFORMANCE - Performance is significantly better than average. Performance consistently exceeds standards.

5. OUTSTANDING - Exceptional performance of unusually high caliber. Remarkable achievement and pacesetting performance.

WEIGHT SCALE:

Each factor will be weighted on a scale from A to C based upon your supervisor's view of its importance to the job you currently have with Heater.

A. A crucial part of the job responsibilities that the employee must concentrate much of his/her time and effort. It is of primary importance.

B. An important part of the job responsibilities. Must spend an adequate amount of time concentrating on it to ensure the job is performed effectively and efficiently.

C. A part of the job responsibilities, although not as critical as several other components. Should not be one of the employee's primary concerns, however, total neglect of it is unacceptable.

1. Job Skills and Knowledge:

Performance
Rating _____

Weight _____

* Demonstrates knowledge & understanding of job duties, equipment and appropriate work methods
* Applies knowledge and skills to produce quality work
* Completes assignments in a thorough and accurate manner
* Uses sound judgement when necessary to reassess projects/or situations
* Able to perform a wide variety of job-related tasks
* Integrates new subject matter into existing operations

Comments: _____
_____

2. Responsibility:

Performance
Rating _____

Weight _____

* Performs responsibilities as specified in the job description
* Performs tasks thoroughly and on time; works within departmental guidelines
* The degree to which the employee and his/her unit/department produce work that is accurate and purposeful
* Make sound recommendations and decisions
* Employee and his/her unit/department completes assigned tasks in designated time periods

Comments: _____
_____

3. Customer Service

Performance
Rating _____

Weight _____

* Maintains courtesy and diplomacy with internal customers and external contacts.
* Makes self available to respond to customer needs
* Prevents unnecessary delays for customers
* When necessary, communicates policies to the customer effectively and accurately
* Listens effectively

Comments: _____
_____

4. **Problem Solving**

* Demonstrates ability to clearly isolate and define problem areas
* Formulates realistic solutions in a timely manner
* Participates constructively in group problem solving
* Considers alternatives and consequences before making decisions
* Presents problems, but offers solutions
* Employee finds innovative and improved ways of doing things and/or generates new ideas
* Employee utilizes job knowledge and sound reasoning to analyze situations, resolve problems, and reach decisions

Performance Rating _____

Weight _____

Comments: _____

5. **Initiative**

* Willing to assume new and challenging assignments
* Expends the effort & time necessary to do the job well
* Routinely shows an interest in improving his/her knowledge and skill level
* When necessary, is able to work independently or within a group
* Offers suggestions to solve problems or improve operations
* Routinely cleans, maintains and repairs his/her equipment and work area

Performance Rating _____

Weight _____

Comments: _____

6. **Management Skills**

* Promotes team work and cooperation
* Trains, coaches, and develops employees
* Delegates responsibility and authority
* Establishes annual goals for the department
* Focuses on achieving results in an effective and timely manner
* Employee communicates and executes company policies
* Clearly defines responsibilities and authority limits to employees
* Recognizes individual capabilities and assigns work accordingly
* Focuses on performance rather than personality in relating to others

Performance Rating _____

Weight _____

Comments: _____

7.   **Leadership Qualities**

	Performance Rating	Weight
	_____	_____

*   Fosters and encourages support from his/her unit/department and/or
    others to accomplish objectives, follow procedures, and accept
    suggestions
*   Inspires confidence and respect in departmental personnel
*   Motivates employees to achieve departmental and business goals
    and objectives
*   Promotes respect, honesty, integrity, and fairness to all

Comments: _____

8.   **Organization**

	Performance Rating	Weight
	_____	_____

*   Adheres to priorities & deadlines; completes work within scheduled
    time frames
*   Follows through on assignments despite setbacks
*   Employee plans and schedules work for him/herself or his/her
    department to ensure Company objectives and goals are met
*   Follows established schedules for work objectives for his/her areas of
    responsibility
*   Eliminates unnecessary duplication
*   Shows a consistently low level of errors
*   Produces neat, accurate, thorough and organized work
*   Demonstrates flexibility in responding to priorities and organizational
    change

Comments: _____

9.   **Budgetary Controls**

	Performance Rating	Weight
	_____	_____

*   Accurately forecasts and maintains budgetary projections
*   Controls operating costs by effectively utilizing staff, materials, and
    equipment
*   Carefully monitors expenditures
*   Contributes to budgetary planning by providing comprehensive
    justification for budgetary requests
*   Meets established time frames for submitting budget requests
    within his/her department
*   Controls capital costs by effectively utilizing staff, materials, and
    equipment

Comments: _____
_____

10. Disciplinary Measures

* Employee is prompt in addressing disciplinary problems
* Employee handles disciplinary measures in an appropriate manner
* Employee equitably reacts and applies disciplinary measures to his/her employees

Performance
Rating   _____

Weight   _____

Comments: _____
_____

11. Attendance & Punctuality

* Reports to work as scheduled
* Follows call-in and approval procedures for time off
* Requests and uses leave appropriately

Performance
Rating   _____

Weight   _____

Comments: _____
_____

12. Interaction with Others

* Expresses ideas and information accurately and understandably in both oral and written form
* Interacts and cooperates with others to ensure the Company's objectives and goals are met
* Resolves conflict effectively
* Shows interest in the job and in the Company
* Promotes departmental teamwork and interdepartmental teamwork
* Has a positive attitude towards his/her work

Performance
Rating   _____

Weight   _____

Comments: _____
_____

13. **Interaction with Supervisor**

* Accepts supervision with a positive & appropriate attitude
* Receives constructive criticism well
* Communicates effectively with Supervisor
* If confused, clarifies policies and work assignments
* Executes direction and plans from Supervisor

Performance
Rating _____

Weight _____

Comments: _____

14. **Organizational Development**

* Promotes and actively participates in OD process
* Solicits ideas from other departments when appropriate
* Contributes to departmental & interdepartmental teamwork
* Supports Company objectives and mission statement

Performance
Rating _____

Weight _____

Comments: _____

15. **Safety and Health**

* Actively participates in and supports the safety and health program
* Enforces all safety and health rules, regulations, and procedures
* Participates in and provides employees with training, demonstrations, and literature on safety practices, procedures, and programs
* Makes certain that equipment, tools, and machinery are being used and maintained properly
* Keeps abreast of accident and injury trends occurring within their department(s) and takes proper corrective action(s) to reverse these trends
* Investigates all accidents, with Safety Coordinator, occurring within their department

Performance
Rating _____

Weight _____

Comments: _____

_____

_____

LIST EMPLOYEE'S STRENGTHS _____

_____

_____

LIST AREAS IN WHICH EMPLOYEE COULD IMPROVE _____

_____

_____

If the employee needs to be put on an "Improvement Work Program", the employee, his/her supervisor, and personnel will create a program that allows the employee time to improve his/her overall performance level. At the end of the specified time limit, the employee and his/her supervisor will have a meeting to discuss employee's improvement.

EMPLOYEE: You must sign this form, thus acknowledging that you and your supervisor have discussed the results. Your signature, however, does not necessarily constitute agreement with the rating.

EMPLOYEE'S SIGNATURE _____

DATE _____

SUPERVISOR'S SIGNATURE _____

DATE _____

8

NOTES AND/OR COMMENTS   (By the employee and/or supervisor)

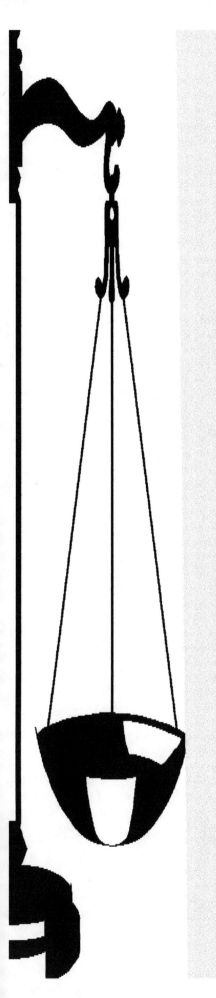

X.

Competency/
Criteria Based
Appraisals

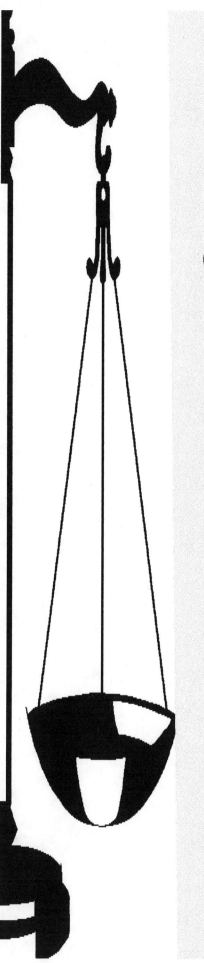

Competency/
Criteria Based #1

189

CRITERIA-BASED PERFORMANCE APPRAISAL

☐ Annual   ☐ Introductory   ☐ Supplementary

Employee Name: _____

Title:_____ Employee Number: _____

Cost Center: _____ Department:_____

A. CUSTOMER SERVICE

Listed below are the components of our Customer Service program. Note whether, for each factor, performance has been **Exceptional** (4 points), **Consistently Above Expectations** (3 points), **Met Expectations** (2 points), **Needs Improvement** (1 point), or **Not Met** (0 points). Refer to the *"Expectations at Anaheim Memorial Hospital"* for more specific rating definitions. ***Add supporting comments for ANY ranking other than "Met Expectations."***

1. First Impression Standards

A. *One to One Encounters:* Promotes a caring and positive image of self and hospital by being well groomed, smiling, making eye contact, calling customer by preferred name, introducing self and having general knowledge of the hospital and its services.

	TO BE COMPLETED BY MANAGER		
Employee	Rating	Weight	Total
		%	

Employee Comments: _____

_____

Supervisor Comments: _____

_____

B. Abides by the *"First Impression Standards"* for General Encounters. This includes: general public encounters, walking in the hallways, on the elevator and when someone enters your area.

	TO BE COMPLETED BY MANAGER		
Employee	Rating	Weight	Total
		%	

Employee Comments: _____

_____

Supervisor Comments: _____

_____

C. Abides by the *"First Impression Standards"* for *telephone usage*. This includes: general telephone etiquette, answering telephone, putting someone on hold, transferring a call and placing a call.

	TO BE COMPLETED BY MANAGER		
Employee	Rating	Weight	Total
		%	

Employee Comments: _____

_____

Supervisor Comments: _____

_____

2. Customers First

A. Always puts the needs of the customer first. Informs customers about department procedures and their role. Treats each person as an individual and is responsive to their needs. Emphasizes to the customer their importance.

	TO BE COMPLETED BY MANAGER		
Employee	Rating	Weight	Total
		%	

Employee Comments: _____

_____

Supervisor Comments: _____

_____

B. Understands it is the collective efforts of all departments that make us successful in the delivery of quality patient care. Defers self interest for the good of patients and the effective operations of the hospital.

TO BE COMPLETED BY MANAGER

Employee ☐

Rating	Weight	Total
☐	☐ %	☐

Employee Comments: _____

Supervisor Comments: _____

3. Interpersonal Skills
A. Possesses good communication skills (personally, by telephone and in writing) and is able to relate well to others.

TO BE COMPLETED BY MANAGER

Employee ☐

Rating	Weight	Total
☐	☐ %	☐

Employee Comments: _____

Supervisor Comments: _____

4. Discuss areas in which Customer Service efforts need to be improved: *Employee –* _____

Supervisor – _____

TO BE COMPLETED BY MANAGER

Summary Score
☐

Summary Score...

B. STANDARDS OF PERFORMANCE – CURRENT YEAR

From duties documented in the Job Description, select the 5 to 8 most critical for successful job performance. For each, document one to two evaluation criteria (state in as specific, quantitative a manner as possible). Use zero to four point scale from Section A to evaluate each factor. *For any factor ranking other than "Met," supporting comments are REQUIRED.*

Position Duty	Expectation/Standard of Performance	0 - 4 Point Scale	Supporting Comments
1.	a.		
	b.		
2.	a.		
	b.		
3.	a.		
	b.		
4.	a.		
	b.		
5.	a.		
	b.		
6.	a.		
	b.		
7.	a.		
	b.		
8.	a.		
	b.		

CHANGES FOR NEXT YEAR: Document any **change** in critical job duties or standards of performance that will be the basis for evaluation next year. Note which of this year's critical job duties, if any, are being replaced by new critical job duties.

Position Duty	Expectation/Standard of Performance
1.	a.
	b.
2.	a.
	b.
3.	a.
	b.
4.	a.
	b.
5.	a.
	b.
6.	a.
	b.

C. KEY SUCCESS FACTORS

Listed below are the capabilities generally required of all employees. Note whether, for each factor, performance has been *Exceptional* (4 points), *Consistently Above Expectations* (3 points), *Met Expectations* (2 points), *Needs Improvement* (1 point), or *Not Met* (0 points). Refer to the *"Expectations at Anaheim Memorial Hospital"* for more specific rating definitions. *For any ranking other than "Met," supporting comments are REQUIRED.*

1. *Supports the Organization...* Understands the vision and mission of Anaheim Memorial Hospital. Realizes how their job function impacts the operation of the organization. Supports the organizational philosophy by demonstrating flexibility, adjusting to changing job demands, dealing creatively and inventively with challenges or problems.

TO BE COMPLETED BY MANAGER

Employee | Rating | Weight | Total
%

Employee Comments: _____

Supervisor Comments: _____

2. *Quality of Work...* Performs job function right the first time. Examines the activities and tasks performed, to ensure they are really meeting the customer requirements. The activities and tasks are done accurately to consistently deliver a useful product.

TO BE COMPLETED BY MANAGER

Employee | Rating | Weight | Total
%

Employee Comments: _____

Supervisor Comments: _____

3. *Work Quantity and Organization...* Possesses organizational abilities to effectively perform assigned work to fulfill job priorities, and to make optimum use of work hours.

TO BE COMPLETED BY MANAGER

Employee | Rating | Weight | Total
%

Employee Comments: _____

Supervisor Comments: _____

4. *Dependability...* Adherence to schedules, punctual, and available to assist in covering last minute scheduling needs. Complies with hospital policy of no more than seven unscheduled absences per year and/or no more than one tardy per pay period.

TO BE COMPLETED BY MANAGER

Employee | Rating | Weight | Total
%

Employee Comments: _____

Supervisor Comments: _____

5. *Safety...* Knowledge and practice of safety policies and procedures to include: Body Mechanics, Employee Safety, Infection Control, Disaster, Fire and Hazardous Materials. Exercises environmental controls to reduce risk of injury.

TO BE COMPLETED BY MANAGER

Employee

Rating	Weight	Total
	%	

Employee Comments: _____

Supervisor Comments: _____

TO BE COMPLETED BY MANAGER

Summary Score

Summary Score ....

D. GOAL ACHIEVEMENT *(For use in appropriate circumstances)*

Referring to the prior year's Performance Appraisal Action Plan (Section F), document the extent to which mutually agreed goals (both day-to-day activity *and* assigned projects, if any) were achieved:

	Goal	0-4 Pt. Scale	Comments
1.			
2.			
3.			

Other Notable Accomplishments: _____

E. PERFORMANCE SUMMARY *(Using zero to 4 point scale)*

1. Customer Service...Summary Score: _____ × .40 = _____
2. Standards of Performance ....Summary Score: _____ × .30 = _____
3. Key Success Factors...Summary Score: _____ × .30 = _____

TOTAL = _____

4. Goal Achievement: (May modify total score above **if** based on prior year's mutually agreed Action Plan. Total score may be modified by no more than .3 up or down.)..............**GRAND TOTAL** = _____

F. ACTION PLAN Document goals (such as special projects, career development needs, operating ratios) which need to be accomplished in the coming year.

	Goal	Measure of Success	When Completed
1.			
2.			
3.			

G. EMPLOYEE COMMENTS

1. We have reviewed the job description for my job and it reflects my job duties... ☐ Yes ☐ No

2. This review is generally consistent with my view of my own performance. .... ☐ Yes ☐ No

3. Other Comments: _____

This appraisal has been discussed with me... *Signature:*_____ *Date:* _____

H. SUPERVISOR'S COMMENTS: _____

Signature: _____ *Date:* _____

TO BE COMPLETED BY HUMAN RESOURCES:			
Current Pay Rate: _____	Salary Increase Granted: _____ %	New Pay Rate: _____	Effective Date: _____

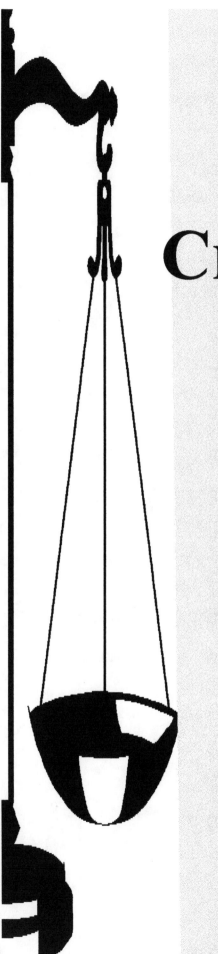

Competency/
Criteria Based #2

POSITION DESCRIPTION / PERFORMANCE EVALUATION

Position: **Secretary/Receptionist**

Employee: _____

Reviewer: _____

Date: _____

Reports To: **Support Services Manager**

Department: **Staff Services**

A Position Description is not intended to be an exhaustive list of ALL responsibilities, skills, efforts and working conditions associated with a job. It is, instead, a description of the principle job elements needed for recruitment, placement, orientation, training, competency assessment, performance appraisal, position classification and other personnel actions.

Individuals with responsibility for the assessment, treatment or care of patients must be able to demonstrate the knowledge and skills necessary to provide the care appropriate to the age of the patients served on his/her unit/department. The individual must demonstrate knowledge of the principles of growth and development over the life span and possess the ability to assess data reflective of the patient's status in addition to being able to interpret the appropriate information needed to identify each patient's requirements relative to his/her age specific needs and to be able to provide the care needed as described in the unit's/department's policies and procedures.

POSITION PURPOSE:

Performs secretarial, reception and other office procedures in support of the functions of the Staff Services Department.

SPECIFICATIONS (Education, Knowledge, Skills, Abilities, Licensure, Certification, Registration):

- Associate Degree in Secretarial Science or Equivalent Experience/Knowledge/Education
- Proficiency in WordPerfect 6.1
- Knowledge of Filing & Office Systems
- Ability to Organize Work and Handle Multiple Projects/Priorities
- Ability to Greet and Serve Visitors in a Manner Conducive to Positive Customer Relations
- Typing Speed of 60+ WPM
- Knowledge of Proper English, Spelling and Grammar
- Ability to Maintain Cooperative Working Relationships

Competency Feeder Report

Overall Level of Experience/Expertise: ❑ Satisfactory   ❑ Marginal   ❑ Unsatisfactory

If Marginal or Unsatisfactory, What Action(s) will be Taken?   ❑ Termination   ❑ Counseling/Discipline

❑ Other (Describe): _____

Remedial Action(s):   **Competency**   **Remedial Action(s)**

_____   _____

_____   _____

Note: This report summarizes results of the "Competency" section of this review. It is NOT a summary of actual performance, which is recorded in other areas of the Review Package. If some components of the Competency evaluation are less than Satisfactory, but overall competence is Satisfactory, the employee should be rated "Satisfactory." Please list competencies that need improvement. Indicate planned actions (educational programs, learning activities, etc.) to improve the person's competence in those areas.

Accountability	Performance Weight	Rating	Competency Level of Experience/Expertise			
			1	2	3	4

(1) Partner Pride (Guest Relations)   Weight: 3   Rating: _____

- Puts Needs of Patients/Customers First
- Listens and Responds to Needs of Patients/Customers
- Keeps Patients and Families Informed
- Respects Patient's Right to Privacy
- Deals with Patients/Customers in a Friendly, Courteous, Sensitive, Helpful and Enthusiastic Manner
- Assists Visitors and Gives Directions
- Displays Pride in Facility/Organization/Department
- Promotes Positive Image of Hospital, Services, Staff
- Maintains Neat, Clean and Professional Personal Appearance
- Takes Appropriate Steps to Solve Patient and Customer Complaints/Problems

(2) Policies and Procedures   Weight: 2   Rating: _____

- Adheres to all Hospital and Departmental Rules, Policies and Procedures
- Maintains Knowledge of and Responds in Accordance with Fire, Mass Casualty and Evacuation Plans
- Maintains Knowledge of and Adheres to All Aspects of Infectious Waste Policy, Employee Exposure Plan and Hazardous Waste Manual
- Operates All Equipment, Uses All Materials and Performs All tasks and Procedures in a Safe and Appropriate Manner
- Adheres to Policy Standards for Attendance
- Maintains Appropriate Levels of Confidentiality Relative to Patient and Other Guarded Information

(3) Participation, Teamwork & Development   Weight: 1   Rating: _____

- Maintains Positive Intra and Inter-Departmental Working Relations
- Adjusts Personal Performance to Team Needs
- Accepts Change and Corrective Counsel
- Accepts Additional/Reduced/Changed Hours & Assignments as Workloads Require
- Accepts and Performs Fair Share of Work/Responsibilities
- Accepts and Follows Supervisory Direction
- Attends Staff Meetings and Inservices as Required
- Uses Initiative to Remain Current & Improve Job Skills

(4) Secretarial   Weight: 3   Rating: _____

- Uses Word Processor and Typewriter to Complete the Following Typing Assignments within Expected Time Frames:
  - Assignments from Supervisor
  - Departmental Form Letters
  - Special Projects as Assigned by Professional Staff
  - Major Mailings
- Assures All Documents and Correspondence are Professional In Appearance and Free of Spelling/Grammatical Errors

Level of Experience/Expertise: 1 = Little or None   2 = Some (May Require Practice/Assistance)
3 = Competent and Experienced   4 = Able to Assess Competency of Others

Accountability	Performance Weight	Rating	Competency Level of Experience/Expertise			
			1	2	3	4

(4) Secretarial (Continued)

- Accumulates and Distributes Mail (In/Out) According to Established Procedures and within Required Time Frames
- Assures All Departmental Filing is Up to Date, Organized and Labeled According to Established Protocol
- Provides Other Secretarial Services to Supervisor as Assigned and within Agreed-Upon Time Frames

(5) Reception   2

- Greets and Manages Visitors Promptly and in Accordance with Established Procedures for Referral and Service
- Answers Phone Within 3 Rings and Completes Contact According to Established Procedures for Referral and Service
- Staffs Reception Area Until Properly Relieved

(6) Clerical   3

- Orders Office Supplies, Assuring Adequate, Well-Organized Level of Inventory
- Assures All Support Filing is Maintained According to Established Protocol
    - Accomplishes Routine Filing Within 2 Days
    - Accomplished Bulk Filing Within 1 Week
- Prepares Assessment Log According to Guidelines
- Accumulates and Burns Confidential Material According to Established Procedures
- Enrolls Public for Special Programs According to Established Procedures and Timetables
- Assembles and Organizes Spector Care Program Materials within Designated Timetables/Deadlines
- Posts BNA Reference Within 14 Days of Receipt
- Logs and Routes Invoice Inquiries According to Guidelines
- Completes Assessment Forms Accurately and Objectively
- Completes Other Clerical Assignments as Directed with Acceptable Quality and Within Agreed-Upon/Established Time Frames

Level of Experience/Expertise: 1 = Little or None   2 = Some (May Require Practice/Assistance)
                                        3 = Competent and Experienced   4 = Able to Assess Competency of Others

POSITION DESCRIPTION / PERFORMANCE EVALUATION
(Addendum)

Age Specific Criteria

Demonstrates Required Knowledge, Skills and Abilities for the Following Patient Populations:

	Neo-Natal			Pediatrics			Adolescence			Adult			Geriatrics		
	Y	N	NA	Y	N	NA	Y	N	NA	Y	N	NA	Y	N	NA
Knowledge of Growth and Development	—	—	—	—	—	—	—	—	—	—	—	—	—	—	—
Ability to Assess Age Specific Data	—	—	—	—	—	—	—	—	—	—	—	—	—	—	—
Ability to Interpret Age Specific Data	—	—	—	—	—	—	—	—	—	—	—	—	—	—	—
Ability to Prove Age Specific Care	—	—	—	—	—	—	—	—	—	—	—	—	—	—	—
Possess Communications Skill Necessary to Interpret Age Specific Response to Treatment	—	—	—	—	—	—	—	—	—	—	—	—	—	—	—
Ability to Involve Family/ Significant Other in Decision Making Related to Plan of Care	—	—	—	—	—	—	—	—	—	—	—	—	—	—	—
_____	—	—	—	—	—	—	—	—	—	—	—	—	—	—	—
_____	—	—	—	—	—	—	—	—	—	—	—	—	—	—	—

Monitored Competencies

Competency Standard	How Met	Date	Level of Experience/Expertise			
			1	2	3	4
_____	____	____	—	—	—	—
_____	____	____	—	—	—	—

(Continued)

Level of Experience/Expertise: 1 = Little or None   2 = Some (May Require Practice/Assistance)
3 = Competent and Experienced   4 = Able to Assess Competency of Others

Monitored Competencies
(Continued)

Competency Standard	How Met	Date	Level of Experience/Expertise			
			1	2	3	4
_____	_____	_____	___	___	___	___
_____	_____	_____	___	___	___	___
_____	_____	_____	___	___	___	___
_____	_____	_____	___	___	___	___
_____	_____	_____	___	___	___	___
_____	_____	_____	___	___	___	___
_____	_____	_____	___	___	___	___
_____	_____	_____	___	___	___	___
_____	_____	_____	___	___	___	___
_____	_____	_____	___	___	___	___

Comments / Notes

Level of Experience/Expertise: 1 = Little or None   2 = Some (May Require Practice/Assistance)
3 = Competent and Experienced   4 = Able to Assess Competency of Others

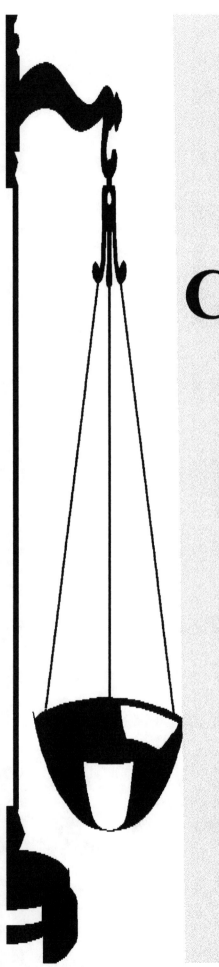

Competency/
Criteria Based #3

PERFORMANCE MANAGEMENT PROCESS

EXEMPT EMPLOYEES PERFORMANCE EVALUATION

FOR:

Name: _____ Location: _____ Supvr.: _____

Title:_____ Grade: _____ Salary: $ _____

Date Last Increase: ____/____/_____   Amount: $ _____

Salary Range

Minimum	1st Quartile	Mid Point	3rd Quartile	Maximum
$	$	$	$	$
Review Period Start:		Review Period End:	Last Review Date:	
Reviewer Name			Reviewer Title	

All Exempt reviews must be scheduled between January 1 and April 1 each year and returned to your local Human Resource Representative no later than April 15.

All salary actions are effective the first pay period in May.

COMPONENTS

Pages 2 and 3 of this document contain definitions of the components, processes and terms used. Pages 4 through 13 include rating forms and the instructions on how to use each form. Pages 14 and 15 are for optional components and attaching supporting data.

The Performance Management Process contains the following components. Some are used throughout the Company with every review. Some are optional and discretionary, and their use is determined by each Division's or functional unit's management and policies.

Check with your local Human Resources Representative for information on which optional components are to be used at your site.

STANDARD COMPONENTS

- **Performance goals.** Every employee's performance is measured against specific goals developed during performance planning meetings with their manager prior to the beginning of each calendar year. Results are reviewed following the end of the year.

- **Core Competencies.** Elkay has identified 28 core competencies critical to our success. Every employee's performance is measured and documented relative to each of these.

- **Critical Management Skills.** For managers and supervisors who have employees reporting to them, additional management skills are measured, documented and evaluated.

OPTIONAL COMPONENTS

- **Annual Personal Development Progress.** Performance against annual personal development goals are reviewed following the end of each calendar year. These goals are developed during personal development planning meetings between employees and their manager.

- **Customer Satisfaction.** For evaluators who want to include customer satisfaction feedback to measure performance, there is the opportunity to document and include the results as a part of the performance evaluation rating. Forms for collection of customer feedback are available from your local Human Resources Representative.

- **Multi-source Assessment.** For those evaluators that desire it Multi-Source Assessment forms are available to collect and document performance relative to the 28 core competencies from multiple sources (Peers, supervisor, customers, self, etc.). The results can be included as a part of the performance evaluation score. Forms for collection of multi-source appraisal are available from your local Human Resources Representative.

PROCESS

The Performance Management Process has two steps: **Performance Planning** and **Performance Evaluation**.

PERFORMANCE PLANNING

PURPOSE

Planning builds the connection between each employee's performance and the overall direction of the Company, Division and Department. It is the foundation of the Performance Management Process.

The performance plan provides:

- Focus and direction for performance.

- A mutually understood set of expectations between managers and their employees.

- Measurements for assessing progress and achievement.

FIVE STEPS

1. The manager holds a planning meeting with each employee prior to or at the beginning of each calendar year.

2. The manager and each employee together draft a performance plan for the calendar year. In doing so, they develop annual goals and identify the core competencies that most directly relate to success of each job.

3. The manager and employee agree on specific expectations for the year.

4. The manager and employee complete the Performance Goals section (Page 4) and the weighting of the Core Competencies section (Pages 7 and 9). Also . the manager indicates to the employee how each performance category will be weighted in the final aggregate rating. (Page 13.)

5. The manager and employee sign the form and the manager keeps the original copy for use in the evaluation meeting following the end of the year.

PERFORMANCE EVALUATION

PURPOSE

The performance evaluation is an opportunity to:

- Review, discuss, evaluate, and document progress toward planned goals.

- Determine methods to improve performance where necessary.

- Evaluate the employee's contribution to the business.

- Set the stage for next year's goals.

THE PROCESS

Annual reviews for each employee are scheduled between January 1 and April 1. All salary increases resulting from the review are effective the first pay period in May.

More frequent performance reviews may be required due to significant changes in the employee's performance.

SEVEN STEPS

1. The manager holds a performance evaluation meeting with each employee.

2. Using the Performance Evaluation forms, the manager documents performance and the evaluation.

3. The manager determines a merit pay action appropriate to the performance evaluation.

4. The manager forwards completed forms to next level of management for approval.

5. The manager and employee meet to review performance and manager advises employee of merit pay action.

6. The manager and employee document their discussion and comments on the review form and sign the form.

7. The completed Performance Evaluation form and Payroll Change Notice form are sent to the local Human Resource Representative.

PERFORMANCE GOALS

Planning Stage

Complete columns (1), (2) and (3) at the beginning of each year during the Performance Planning meeting. Complete column (4) during the Performance Evaluation.

Planning Completed On _____ Employee Signature _____

Manager Signature _____

(1) Objective	(2) Method of Measurement	(3) 199__ Goal	(4) 199__ Result

Evaluation Stage
Reviewer is to assign a rating using the scale below based on actual performance documented above.

Rating(1-5):_____ Date:_____

Comments on Rating

SCALE

5 = Far Exceeded Expectations	4 = Exceeded Expectations	3 = Met Expectations	2 = Below Expectations	1 = Far Below Expectations

CORE COMPETENCIES RATING INSTRUCTIONS

Performance Planning

During the Performance Planning meeting prior to the beginning of each year, the manager and employee together **weight** the importance of each competency using the IMPORTANCE TO THE JOB scale below and insert the ratings on pages 7 and 9

Performance Evaluation

During the Performance Evaluation following the end of the year, the reviewing manager indicates the PROFICIENCY level for each competency using the scale below and inserting the ratings on pages 7 and 9. Multiply the importance rating by the proficiency rating to determine the weighted rating for each competency. On page 9 the total weighted score is to be calculated using the formula as shown. Space is also available for evaluators comments.

CORE COMPETENCY PERFORMANCE RATING SCALE:

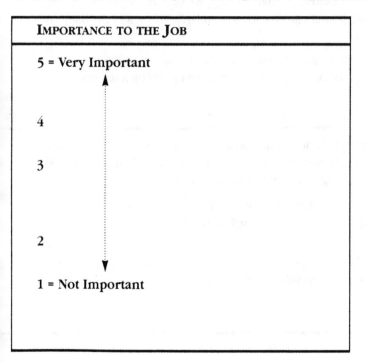

IMPORTANCE TO THE JOB
5 = Very Important
4
3
2
1 = Not Important

PROFICIENCY SCALE
5 = Able to deal effectively and in a superior manner with virtually all situations involving the competency area and can serve as a coach or mentor to others in its application.
4 = Able to deal effectively in an above average manner with most situations involving the competency.
3 = Able to deal effectively with routine, day-to-day, situations involving the competency area, but needs help in dealing with particularly difficult situations involving the competency.
2 = Has some level of skill in competency, but needs help with most situations.
1 = Has virtually no acceptable level of skill in competency.

CORE COMPETENCIES DEFINITIONS

STRATEGIC ORGANIZATIONAL SKILLS

1. **Focuses on the Customer:** Consistently demonstrates awareness that our customers enable us to thrive as a business; understands each customer's needs and uses that knowledge to anticipate problems and provide even better service than the customer expects; treats internal customers with the same high level of service as external customers; looks for new opportunities to enhance customer satisfaction.

2. **Knows the Business:** Understands and stays abreast of issues and events that have an impact on our business and industry; gains insight into the ways that key events could impact our business goals and the environment in which we operate.

3. **Focuses on Systems and Processes:** Emphasizes that our business is a set of systems and processes; identifies and implements effective processes and procedures to reduce cycle time, increase quality, and add value to the business.

4. **Measures Results:** Builds methods for measuring how effectively processes meet business objectives; uses fact-based information to make decisions.

5. **Focuses on Profitability:** Emphasizes the fundamental importance of contributing to profitability; chooses courses of action that will enhance our financial strength, now and in the future.

6. **Commits to Quality:** Demonstrates personal responsibility for delivering high quality products and services; sets high personal standards for quality, and measures every activity and product against those standards; adheres to the highest standards of performance throughout the development process.

7. **Promotes Corporate Citizenship:** Performs day-to-day activities and job responsibilities in ways that support the company's commitment to add value to and not diminish the quality of life in the communities in which we operate.

THINKING SKILLS

8. **Analyzes and Solves Problems:** Conducts a thorough search for relevant information when approaching problems; grasps pertinent issues in all their complexity; carefully weighs the impact of a broad range of related issues or factors; requests the opinions and insights of others during problem-solving efforts, when appropriate.

9. **Makes Sound Decisions:** Makes high quality decisions in a timely manner, even under uncertain conditions; considers both the immediate and the long-term consequences of decisions; makes decisions that support the mission, strategies, and objectives of our business.

10. **Thinks Creatively:** Generates new ideas and initiative; challenges the status quo in thought and action, when appropriate; inspires creative thinking in others, and considers their ideas and suggestions with an open mind.

LEADERSHIP SKILLS

11. **Manages Team Efforts:** Clearly conveys goals and expectations to others involved in projects; is available to provide support and up-to-date information to others when needed; coordinates efforts with other groups; monitors progress made toward goals.

12. **Leads Courageously:** Steps forward to confront difficult issues; takes personal responsibility for resolving those issues; demonstrates determination and fearlessness when important issues are at stake.

13. **Influences Others:** Communicates ideas persuasively; gains support and commitment from others; negotiates effectively; inspires others to take action; leads by example.

14. **Champions Change:** Questions assumptions and supports creative proposals for doing things a better way; paves the way for positive change; diminishes fear and persuades others to let go of resistance and embrace change.

CORE COMPETENCIES RATING

STRATEGIC ORGANIZATIONAL SKILLS

	Importance	Proficiency	Weighted Total
1. Focuses on the Customer	_____	_____	_____
2. Knows the Business	_____	_____	_____
3. Focuses on Systems & Processes	_____	_____	_____
4. Measures Results	_____	_____	_____
5. Focuses on Profitability	_____	_____	_____
6. Commits to Quality	_____	_____	_____
7. Promotes Corporate Citizenship	_____	_____	_____

COMMENTS

THINKING SKILLS

	Importance	Proficiency	Weighted Total
8. Analyzes and Solves Problems	_____	_____	_____
9. Makes Sound Decisions	_____	_____	_____
10. Thinks Creatively	_____	_____	_____

LEADERSHIP SKILLS

	Importance	Proficiency	Weighted Total
11. Manages Team Efforts	_____	_____	_____
12 Leads Courageously	_____	_____	_____
13. Influences Others	_____	_____	_____
14. Champions Change	_____	_____	_____

CORE COMPETENCIES DEFINITIONS

INTERPERSONAL SKILLS

15. **Builds Relationships:** Fosters alliances with others as valuable resources; treats others with respect and dignity; seeks to understand other people's viewpoints.

16. **Develops Networks:** Links up with others in formal and informal networks to share information and reach mutual goals; builds a strong network of relationships outside the Company with others in the same industry or profession.

17. **Works Well on a Team:** Demonstrates commitment to shared team goals; encourages all team members to contribute their ideas and skills; values the contributions of others; fulfills responsibility to the team by doing an equal share of the work; balances personal interests with the needs of the team.

18. **Helps Others:** Encourages and supports others in reaching their goals; is sensitive to the needs of others and generously helps out when needed.

COMMUNICATION SKILLS

19. **Communicates Effectively:** Speaks clearly and concisely, expresses thoughts and ideas easily in groups and in one-to-one conversations; adapts communication style to fit the audience, in order to keep their attention and enhance their understanding.

20. **Listens to Others:** Shows interest in what others have to say; listens attentively to their questions and comments; expresses appreciation for others' points of view; listens well in a group to enhance understanding and quality of participation.

MOTIVATION

21. **Strives to Achieve:** Works hard to succeed and achieve optimal results; acts with a sense of urgency to create momentum and see projects through to completion; forges ahead to overcome obstacles and opposition.

22. **Shows Commitment:** Displays unwavering attention to high standards of performance; pursues challenging goals in the face of adversity; perseveres even when confronted with setbacks.

23. **Takes Initiative:** Acts quickly and independently when the situation demands it; sees a need and takes appropriate action without being prompted or reminded; proactively recommends process improvements or solutions to problems.

SELF-MANAGEMENT SKILLS

24. **Works Efficiently:** Organizes own time effectively; maximizes the use of available resources; successfully balances the competing demands of multiple projects by setting priorities and communicating and meeting deadlines; strives to eliminate inefficient work habits or processes; ask for help when necessary.

25. **Acts With Integrity:** Approaches all business decisions and actions guided by sound personal and professional ethics; consistently behaves in ways that reflect the company's core principles and values; earns the trust of others by dealing with them honestly and following through on commitments.

26. **Demonstrates Adaptability:** Recovers quickly when progress is stalled by obstacles or adversity; responds with flexibility and resilience when faced with multiple demands, shifting priorities, ambiguity, and rapid change.

27. **Takes Calculated Risks:** Draws on personal experiences and factual information when calculating the risks involved in business decisions; capitalizes on opportunities that contain an acceptable level of risk, after thoughtful analysis.

28. **Pursues Personal Development:** Continually learns from personal experience; actively seeks opportunities for learning and self-development; requests feedback and welcomes advice when it's offered; alters behavior to reflect new insights and changing circumstances.

CORE COMPETENCIES RATING

INTERPERSONAL SKILLS

	Importance	Proficiency	Weighted Total
15. Builds Relationships	_____	_____	_____
16 Develops Networks	_____	_____	_____
17. Works well on a Team	_____	_____	_____
18. Helps Others	_____	_____	_____

COMMUNICATION SKILLS

COMMENTS

	Importance	Proficiency	Weighted Total
19. Communicates Effectively	_____	_____	_____
20. Listens to Others	_____	_____	_____

MOTIVATION

	Importance	Proficiency	Weighted Total
21. Strives to Achieve	_____	_____	_____
22. Shows Commitment	_____	_____	_____
23. Takes Initiative	_____	_____	_____

SELF-MANAGEMENT SKILLS

	Importance	Proficiency	Weighted Total
24. Works Efficiently	_____	_____	_____
25 Acts With Integrity	_____	_____	_____
26. Demonstrates Adaptability	_____	_____	_____
27. Takes Calculated Risks	_____	_____	_____
28. Pursues Personal Development	_____	_____	_____

TABULATION

	Importance	Proficiency	Weighted Total			
				Weighted Average	=	Weighted Total / Importance Total
TOTAL	_____	_____	_____	Weighted Average	=	_____

9

CRITICAL MANAGEMENT SKILLS RATING

NOTE: For each Critical Management Skill indicated on the following questionnaire, the rating manager must indicate the level of proficiency on a scale of 1 to 5 as defined below. The scores are to be totaled and then an average calculated and documented in the space indicated.

CRITICAL MANAGEMENT SKILLS

PROFICIENCY
(1-5)

_____ 1. **Establish Plans.** Develops plans that are appropriately comprehensive, realistic and effective in meeting objectives; accurately assesses resource needs; develops contingency plans when necessary. Integrates planning efforts across work units. Involves employees in planning and change.

_____ 2. **Structure and Staff.** Recruits and hires the most appropriate people for permanent and temporary assignments; builds a strong team with complimentary strengths; provides for staff continuity; forms effective structures and teams.

_____ 3. **Develop Systems and Processes.** Identifies and implements effective processes and procedures for accomplishing work. Reduces number of operations, components and transactions. Reduces waiting time between operations, distance between operations and inventory all along process chain.

_____ 4. **Manage Work Activities.** Assigns responsibilities appropriately; delegates to and empowers others; removes obstacles; allows for and contributes needed resources.

_____ 5. **Coordinate Execution.** Makes it easier for employees to do their jobs without error. Conveys clear goals and expectations for direct reports and others involved in projects; is accessible and provides support and up-to-date knowledge to others; coordinates work efforts with other groups; monitors progress. Evaluates performance and takes action when performance falls below expectations.

_____ 6. **Coach and Develop Direct Reports.** Accurately assesses strengths and development needs of Direct Reports. Gives timely, specific feedback; provides challenging assignments and opportunities for development. Willingly shares knowledge and experience with others; provides effective training and explanations when necessary. Ensures that front line employees are trained and empowered to solve their own problems, before management and staff experts.

_____ 7. **Measure for Results and Control.** Establishes measurable criteria in support of organizational objectives; uses fact based information to make decisions and take corrective actions. Trains and coaches employees to record and own process data, and reviews such data with employees on a regularly scheduled basis.

TOTAL _____

÷7

AVERAGE SCORE _____

PROFICIENCY SCALE:

5 = Able to deal effectively and in a superior manner with virtually all situations involving the competency area and can serve as a coach or mentor to others in its application.

4 = Able to deal effectively in an above average manner with most situations involving the competency area.

3 = Able to deal effectively with routine, day-to-day, situations involving the competency area, but needs help in dealing with particularly difficult situations involving the competency area.

2 = Has some level of skill in competency area, but needs help with most situations.

1 = Has virtually no acceptable level of skill in competency area.

EVALUATOR COMMENTS

CRITICAL MANAGEMENT SKILLS

PLANS FOR IMPROVEMENT

The Performance Evaluation process is an opportunity to identify employee strengths and weaknesses. In areas where improvement can be made the reviewing manager and employee need to make specific plans and commitments. These plans and commitments can be documented below.

Additionally, the space below can be used during the Performance Planning meeting at the beginning of the year to document personal improvement activities for the year.

COMMITMENT	COMPLETION DATE

EMPLOYEE COMMENTS

It is important that the reviewed employee document their thoughts and feelings regarding the results of the evaluation and disagreements, if any. The reviewed employee can comment in the space below.

PERFORMANCE RESULTS SUMMARY

Each section of the Performance Evaluation must be assigned a weight before calculating the total score. The weight is the percent each section is to contribute to the total score. The sum of all percentages must equal 100%. Transfer the ratings for each section to the appropriate column below. Multiply the WEIGHT by the RATING for each section to determine the WEIGHTED SCORE. The sum of the WEIGHTED SCORE is the TOTAL PERFORMANCE LEVEL. It will range from 1 to 5, with 5 being the highest score. This score is used to help determine merit pay increase.

Module	(1-100%) Weight x	(1 - 5) Rating	=Weighted Score
Performance Goals			
Core Competencies			
Critical Management Skills			
Annual Personal Development Goals*			
Customer Satisfaction*			
Multi-Source Assessment*			
Performance Level (Weighted Average)	*(Must equal 100%)*		*(Add Weighted Scores)*

* *Optional Components*

This Review has been discussed with me.

Employee
Signature: _____ Date: _____

Evaluator
Signature: _____ Date: _____

Authorization: _____ Date: _____
(Next Level Above Reviewer)

SCORING LEGEND

Numeric Score	Definition
5	Highest
4	↑
3	
2	↓
1	Lowest

ANNUAL PERSONAL DEVELOPMENT PROGRESS

Contact your local Human Resources represent◼
regarding completion of this form.

Planning Stage

Complete columns (1), (2) and (3) at the beginning of each year during the Performance Planning meeting. Complete column (4) during the Performance Evaluation.

Planning Completed On _____ Employee Signature _____

Manager Signature _____

	(1)	(2)	(3)	(4)
	Objective	Method of Measurement	199__ Goal	199__ Resul◼
1.				
2.				
3.				
4.				
5.				

Evaluation Stage

Reviewer is to assign a rating using the scale below based on actual performance documented above.

Rating(1-5): _____ Date: _____

Comments on Rating

<u>SCALE</u>

5 = *Far Exceeded Expectations*   **4** = *Exceeded Expectations*   **3** = *Met Expectations*   **2** = *Below Expectations*   **1** = *Far Below Expectations*

OPTIONAL COMPONENT/SUPPORTING DOCUMENTS

NOTE: Please Attach Here Any Additional Information and/or Optional Performance Evaluation Components such as:

- Customer Satisfaction

- Multi-Source Assessment

220

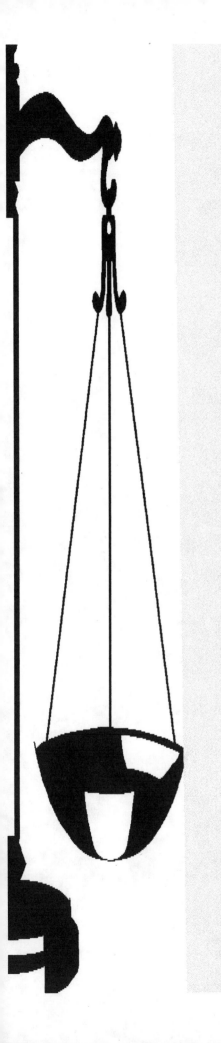

XI.

360 Degree Feedback Appraisals

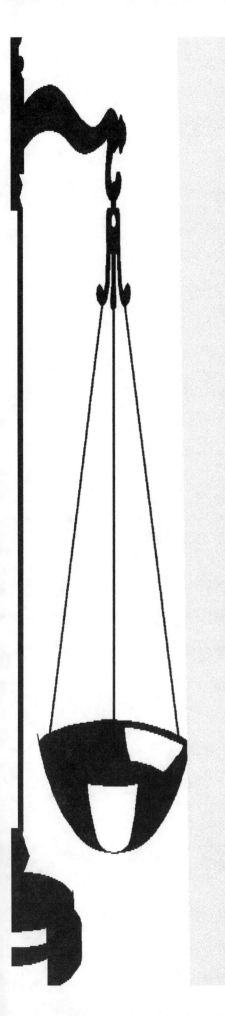

360 Degree #1

ASSOCIATE PROGRESS AND DEVELOPMENT REPORT

ASSOCIATE:_____POSITION:_____

MANAGER:_____DATE OF LAST PROGRESS REPORT:_____

INSTRUCTIONS

STEP 1:

AT THE BEGINNING OF THE REVIEW PERIOD, MEET WITH THE ASSOCIATE TO ESTABLISH JOB PERFORMANCE GOALS AND IMPORTANCE FACTORS. LIST THE GOALS AND IMPORTANCE FACTORS ON PAGE 3, STARTING WITH THE GOAL THAT CARRIES THE HIGHEST IMPORTANCE FACTOR. (NOTE: THE TOTAL AMOUNT OF IMPORTANCE FACTORS MUST NOT EXCEED 50 POINTS, INCLUDING MANAGER AND PEER EVALUATION, WHICH CARRY A MINIMUM OF 5 POINTS AND 3 POINTS, RESPECTIVELY.)

IDENTIFY THE PEERS THAT WILL PARTICIPATE IN THE PEER REVIEW DURING THIS REPORTING PERIOD, AND LIST THEIR NAMES AT THE BOTTOM OF PAGE 3.

ASSOCIATE, MANAGER AND ENDORSER SIGN THE TOP OF PAGE 3. GIVE COPY TO ASSOCIATE.

STEP 2:

ABOUT 45 DAYS PRIOR TO THE CLOSE OF THE REVIEW PERIOD, DELIVER A COPY OF FORM I, "PERFORMANCE IMPROVEMENT DISCUSSION INTERVIEWS," TO THE SELECTED PEERS. REQUEST THAT THEY COMPLETE AND RETURN WITHIN 10 DAYS. ONCE ALL FORMS HAVE BEEN RETURNED, SUMMARIZE THEIR COMMENTS AND RATINGS ON FORM II, "SUMMARY OF PERFORMANCE IMPROVEMENT DISCUSSION INTERVIEWS."

USING THE SATISFACTION DEFINITIONS ON PAGE 2, ENTER THE APPROPRIATE RATINGS FOR JOB PERFORMANCE GOALS AND MANAGER AND PEER EVALUATIONS UNDER COLUMN C ON PAGE 3. MULTIPLY THE PERFORMANCE RATING BY THE IMPORTANCE FACTOR AND ENTER THE RESULT UNDER COLUMN D. TALLY ALL POINTS EARNED (COLUMN D). MULTIPLY EACH IMPORTANCE FACTOR BY 2 (THE HIGHEST AVAILABLE PERFORMANCE RATING) AND ENTER UNDER COLUMN E. THE TOTAL MAXIMUM SATISFACTION POINTS MUST EQUAL 100. DIVIDE THE TOTAL POINTS EARNED BY THE TOTAL MAXIMUM SATISFACTION POINTS. THE RESULT IS THE ASSOCIATE'S ACTUAL PERFORMANCE AGAINST PERFORMANCE GOALS.

EXCEEDS EXPECTATIONS: (2 Points)

Associate's performance **consistently exceeds** performance criteria or standards for all aspects of this Job Performance Goal. Associate performs even the difficult and complex parts of the goal competently and thoroughly, including extra or unique tasks associated with said goal. In measurable accomplishments, Associate's productivity regularly surpasses the required output. Decisions and recommendations are usually sound and may involve high-risk areas. In terms of what is inherently possible in meeting this goal, Associate is innovative and initiates, plans for, accurately prioritizes and accomplishes the goal, and often takes action on his/her own to implement solutions without requiring prior direction.

MEETS EXPECTATIONS: (1 Point)

Associate's performance **fully meets** performance criteria or standards for practically all aspects of this Job Performance Goal. In measurable accomplishments, Associate's productivity generally meets and may occasionally surpass the required output. The Associate's performance is steady, reliable and competent. Decisions and recommendations are usually sound and generally in the moderate risk or structured areas within the goal. While Associate may exercise initiative and innovation in meeting the goal, guidance and direction may be warranted to assist Associate in prioritizing duties and maintaining productivity schedules.

DOES NOT MEET EXPECTATIONS: (0 Points)

Associate's performance **does not meet** the performance criteria or standards of the aspects of this Job Performance Goal. Goals are not achieved or are met with only a minimum level of acceptability. In measurable accomplishments, Associate's productivity is consistently below the required output. Associate is usually reluctant to take action on his/her own unless specifically directed. Associate is reluctant to make decisions or recommendations, or if made, they are often not sound and are usually low-risk or highly routine. **Corrective action is necessary to improve the rating within the next reporting period**.

An overall "Does Not Meet Expectations" rating may mean retention of the Associate in this position is not warranted. At the Company's discretion, the Associate will be placed on probation for a period not to exceed 90 days, at which time the Associate's performance will be re-evaluated. If performance has not improved upon expiration of the probationary period, the Associate will be deemed not qualified for the position. In such case, the Associate may be transferred to a position where a better probability for successful performance exists, if such a position is available within the Company. Or, at the Company's discretion, the Associate's employment will be terminated.

Associate and Manager have set the following job performance goals to be completed within the review period _____ to _____, 19____. The following importance factors have been assigned.

Signed: _____   Signed: _____   Approved: _____

Associate   Date   Manager   Date   Endorser   Date

Column A	Column B	Column C	Column D	Column E
			Points	Maximum
	Importance	Performance	Earned	Satisfaction
	Factor (Max.	Rating	(Col. B X	Points
Job Performance Goals	50 Pts Total)	(2, 1 or 0)	Col. C)	(Col. B X 2)

Manager Evaluation (Min. 5 Points)
Peer Evaluation (Min. 3 Points)
(LIST PEERS HERE)

Totals

OVERALL PERFORMANCE PERCENTAGE AGAINST GOALS (Col. D divided by Col. E)   ═══════════

227

PERFORMANCE vs. GOALS SCHEDULE

Actual Performance % Against Goals	Equivalent Satisfaction Standard	% of Increase	
		12 Months	6 Months
85 - 100%	Exceeds Expectations	7% - 11%	3.5% - 5.5%
40 - 84%	Meets Expectations	3% - 6%	1.5% - 3%
0 - 39%	Does Not Meet Expectations	0%	0%

MANAGER'S COMMENTS

_____

_____

Salary Range for Position of _____ Min $_____ Mid $_____ Max $_____

Associate's **Current** Annual Salary $_____

Increase Percentage / Amount   _____% $_____

Associate's **New** Annual Salary $_____

Date of Next Progress and Development Report   _____

Date_____   **Manager's Signature**_____

ENDORSER'S COMMENTS

_____

_____

Date_____   **Endorser's Signature**_____

ASSOCIATE'S COMMENTS

_____

_____

My signature means that I have discussed the contents of this Progress and Development Report with my Manager and have received a copy. It is not necessarily meant to imply that I agree with either the Overall Performance Percentage Against Goals, nor the comments contained within this Report.

Date_____   **Associate's Signature**_____

9/94

h:\home\scall\performn\progdevl

DATE:

PERFORMANCE IMPROVEMENT DISCUSSION INTERVIEW

ASSOCIATE:	INTERVIEWEE:
	_____

INSTRUCTIONS

Please answer the following questions honestly and openly. **Please be as specific as you can**. Attach another sheet if you need more space. The feedback you share will help us in working with the Associate to enhance and improve his/her performance and boost skills. Your comments will be shared with your Peer; however, your identity and this form will be kept confidential.

1. What specific services, support, reports, projects, etc. do you receive from or work on with this Associate? What is your overall level of satisfaction? What suggestions can you offer that would help him/her improve performance?

General Comments:

2. What skills or knowledge, if improved, would help him/her become more effective in performing his/her job?

General Comments:

3. Please identify any processes, systems and/or organizational issues that prevent/hinder him/her from doing his/her job.

    General Comments:

4. In addition to his/her usual responsibilities in the past year, what special project(s) has he/she worked on that required considerable additional effort? What specific contribution did he/she make to the project's success?

    General Comments:

5. What suggestions would you have to improve the communication, either written or oral, between you and this Associate?

    General Comments:

6. What are your observations as to his/her effectiveness in operating as a team member? What could he/she do to become more effective?

    General Comments:

7. What are your observations as to his/her effectiveness in responding to customer problems, issues and/or complaints? What could he/she do to become more effective?

    General Comments:

INSTRUCTIONS

Check the box that best matches your evaluation of your Peer's conduct. In deciding your answer, carefully consider how your Peer behaves MOST OF THE TIME. In the COMMENTS section of each category, please give specific examples of your Peer's behavior that support your rating. **Examples must be given or the rating will be deemed invalid**. The results of your evaluation will be shared with your Peer; however, your identity and this form will be kept confidential.

Definitions:

Exceeds Requirements -- Associate's performance **consistently exceeds** what is required of him/her to complete assignments. His/her work product is usually error-free, detailed and clear. Deadlines are usually met before their due date, and Associate takes necessary action to avoid possible delays. Associate generally goes beyond what is expected in assisting other Associates and in providing and sharing information and offering solutions, thereby increasing communication, respect, harmony and teamwork within the organization.

Meets Requirements -- Associate's performance **consistently meets** the demands placed upon his/her position in terms of assisting other Associates and providing and sharing information. His/her work product is usually acceptable, but may occasionally require minor revisions. While his/her performance is steady, reliable and competent, prompting, guidance and/or direction may be required for Associate to produce what is required of him/her. Associate usually meets deadlines within his/her control, but if deadlines are missed, Associate willingly attempts to correct the problem to avoid delays in the future.

Below Requirements -- Associate's performance **does not meet** the demands placed upon his/her position. Work product is frequently unacceptable and/or requires major revisions, or output is below standard, causing delays in production. Associate appears reluctant to take action on his/her own without prompting, guidance or direction from other work groups. Deadlines within Associate's control are usually not met. Associate appears to make no effort to correct the problem to avoid future delays, or to provide or share information with other Associates.

	Exceeds Requiremnts	Meets Requiremnts	Below Requiremnts
1. The overall quality of Associate's work product that affects your job	❏	❏	❏

Comments:

2. Associate's overall timeliness in meeting deadlines that affect your job	❏	❏	❏

Comments:

3. Associate's overall ability and attempt to share relevant information with you that has a direct impact on your job	❏	❏	❏

Comments:

	Exceeds Requiremnts	Meets Requiremnts	Below Requiremnts
4. Associate's overall dependability and reliability in following through on commitments to you	❑	❑	❑

Comments:

5. Associate's overall promptness in responding to your needs, questions and/or requests	❑	❑	❑

Comments:

6. Associate's overall promptness in responding to customer needs, questions and/or requests	❑	❑	❑

Comments:

7. Associate's overall friendliness and willingness to assist you with projects and/or meeting deadlines	❑	❑	❑

Comments:

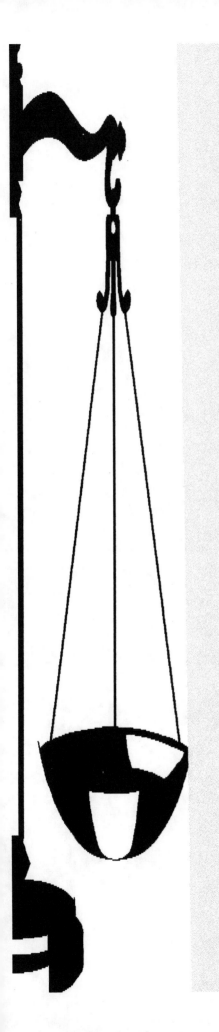

360 Degree #2

Feedback
Request for
Leadership Behaviors

You have been selected to provide feedback for the person identified below. Please use this form to provide feedback about the leadership behaviors which this person demonstrates on a regular basis. The recipient of this feedback will see only a roll-up of the results, not the actual feedback forms.

Name of Feedback Recipient: _____

Name of Evaluator (Optional): _____

Please return the completed form to: _____

                       By_____

Relationship to Feedback Recipient (check one):

❏ Manager   ❏ Peer   ❏ Self

❏ Direct Report   ❏ Below Direct Report   ❏ Internal Customer

Instructions:

      Please indicate the rating that corresponds to the degree to which you observe this person demonstrating the listed leadership behavior, according to the rating key at the top of each page. N/O should be used if you have not been in situations which would afford you the opportunity to observe the behavior.

      At the end of each section, please provide comments and examples which support your ratings. If you need more space for comments, please attach an additional page. Please be sure to include examples for ratings below 3 or above 7. On back panel, please answer questions 9 and 10 according to your experience and relationship with the feedback recipient.

If you have questions, please contact the manager of the feedback recipient.

Feedback Request for Leadership Behaviors

N/O=Not Observed   1=Never   3=Seldom   5=Sometimes   7=Most of the time   10=Always

1.   Inspires a Shared Vision

1.1 Provides direction around a vision   N/O ① ② ③ ④ ⑤ ⑥ ⑦ ⑧ ⑨ ⑩

1.2 Translates the corporate vision into actionable plans   N/O ① ② ③ ④ ⑤ ⑥ ⑦ ⑧ ⑨ ⑩

1.3 Creates enthusiasm about the Future of (your company)   N/O ① ② ③ ④ ⑤ ⑥ ⑦ ⑧ ⑨ ⑩

1.4 Shows others how their long-term Interests can be realized by enlisting In a common vision   N/O ① ② ③ ④ ⑤ ⑥ ⑦ ⑧ ⑨ ⑩

Please explain: (examples required for ratings below 3 and above 7)

_____

_____

_____

_____

2.   Delivers Results

2.1 Makes appropriate decisions   N/O ① ② ③ ④ ⑤ ⑥ ⑦ ⑧ ⑨ ⑩

2.2 Acts after making a decision   N/O ① ② ③ ④ ⑤ ⑥ ⑦ ⑧ ⑨ ⑩

2.3 Takes risks   N/O ① ② ③ ④ ⑤ ⑥ ⑦ ⑧ ⑨ ⑩

2.4 Encourages others to take risks   N/O ① ② ③ ④ ⑤ ⑥ ⑦ ⑧ ⑨ ⑩

2.5 Supports the decisions of others   N/O ① ② ③ ④ ⑤ ⑥ ⑦ ⑧ ⑨ ⑩

Please explain: (examples required for ratings below 3 and above 7)

_____

_____

_____

3. Focuses on the Customer

3.1 Anticipates customer needs   N/O ① ② ③ ④ ⑤ ⑥ ⑦ ⑧ ⑨ ⑩

3.2 Seeks customer feedback   N/O ① ② ③ ④ ⑤ ⑥ ⑦ ⑧ ⑨ ⑩

3.3 Responds to customer feedback   N/O ① ② ③ ④ ⑤ ⑥ ⑦ ⑧ ⑨ ⑩

3.4 Models customer focus in interactions with customers   N/O ① ② ③ ④ ⑤ ⑥ ⑦ ⑧ ⑨ ⑩

3.5 Helps remove barriers to excellent Customer services   N/O ① ② ③ ④ ⑤ ⑥ ⑦ ⑧ ⑨ ⑩

Please explain: (examples required for ratings below 3 and above 7)

_____

_____

_____

_____

4. Challenges the Process

4.1 Pursues better ways to get things done   N/O ① ② ③ ④ ⑤ ⑥ ⑦ ⑧ ⑨ ⑩

4.2 Models breakthrough thinking   N/O ① ② ③ ④ ⑤ ⑥ ⑦ ⑧ ⑨ ⑩

4.3 Acts as a change agent   N/O ① ② ③ ④ ⑤ ⑥ ⑦ ⑧ ⑨ ⑩

4.4 Helps others manage through change N/O ① ② ③ ④ ⑤ ⑥ ⑦ ⑧ ⑨ ⑩

Please explain: (examples required for ratings below 3 and above 7)

_____

_____

_____

_____

5. Values People

5.1 Shows respect for others and their ideas   N/O ① ② ③ ④ ⑤ ⑥ ⑦ ⑧ ⑨ ⑩

5.2 Encourages others' involvement in making things better   N/O ① ② ③ ④ ⑤ ⑥ ⑦ ⑧ ⑨ ⑩

5.3 Appreciates differences between people in thought and style　N/O　① ② ③ ④ ⑤ ⑥ ⑦ ⑧ ⑨ ⑩

5.4 Allows for flexibility in how work is Accomplished　N/O　① ② ③ ④ ⑤ ⑥ ⑦ ⑧ ⑨ ⑩

5.5 Considers others' needs when making decisions　N/O　① ② ③ ④ ⑤ ⑥ ⑦ ⑧ ⑨ ⑩

Please explain: (examples required for ratings below 3 and above 7)

_____
_____
_____
_____

6.　Develops Self and Others

6.1 Demonstrates personal growth and learning　N/O　① ② ③ ④ ⑤ ⑥ ⑦ ⑧ ⑨ ⑩

6.2 Encourages continuous growth & learning in others　N/O　① ② ③ ④ ⑤ ⑥ ⑦ ⑧ ⑨ ⑩

6.3 Acknowledges mistakes & learns from them　N/O　① ② ③ ④ ⑤ ⑥ ⑦ ⑧ ⑨ ⑩

6.4 Sets clear performance expectations in advance　N/O　① ② ③ ④ ⑤ ⑥ ⑦ ⑧ ⑨ ⑩

6.5 Shares positive performance feedback that is timely and direct　N/O　① ② ③ ④ ⑤ ⑥ ⑦ ⑧ ⑨ ⑩

6.6 Shares negative performance that is timely and direct　N/O　① ② ③ ④ ⑤ ⑥ ⑦ ⑧ ⑨ ⑩

6.7 Sends candid messages that are focused on the issue not the person　N/O　① ② ③ ④ ⑤ ⑥ ⑦ ⑧ ⑨ ⑩

Please explain: (examples required for ratings below 3 and above 7)

_____
_____
_____
_____

7.   Communicates with Candor

7.1 Communicates effectively and   N/O   ① ② ③ ④ ⑤ ⑥ ⑦ ⑧ ⑨ ⑩
continuously

7.2 Listens to what others have to say   N/O   ① ② ③ ④ ⑤ ⑥ ⑦ ⑧ ⑨ ⑩

7.3 Shares opinions even when   N/O   ① ② ③ ④ ⑤ ⑥ ⑦ ⑧ ⑨ ⑩
unpopular

7.4 Expresses disagreement earlier   N/O   ① ② ③ ④ ⑤ ⑥ ⑦ ⑧ ⑨ ⑩
than later

7.5 Makes others feel safe in honestly   N/O   ① ② ③ ④ ⑤ ⑥ ⑦ ⑧ ⑨ ⑩
expressing themselves

Please explain: (examples required for ratings below 3 and above 7)

_____

_____

_____

_____

8.   Acts in the Best Interest of the Company and the Enterprise

8.1 Is visible, with positive   N/O   ① ② ③ ④ ⑤ ⑥ ⑦ ⑧ ⑨ ⑩
Presence

8.2 Is highly ethical and professional   N/O   ① ② ③ ④ ⑤ ⑥ ⑦ ⑧ ⑨ ⑩

8.3 Is an effective team member   N/O   ① ② ③ ④ ⑤ ⑥ ⑦ ⑧ ⑨ ⑩

8.4 Instills effective team membership   N/O   ① ② ③ ④ ⑤ ⑥ ⑦ ⑧ ⑨ ⑩
in others

8.5 Models collaboration   N/O   ① ② ③ ④ ⑤ ⑥ ⑦ ⑧ ⑨ ⑩

8.6 Gets involved in making things   N/O   ① ② ③ ④ ⑤ ⑥ ⑦ ⑧ ⑨ ⑩
Better in the company and community

Please explain: (examples required for ratings below 3 and above 7)

_____

_____

_____

_____

9.   What 2-3 behaviors would you like to see this person do differently?

More of?

Less Of?

10.   What 2-3 behaviors would you this person to continue?

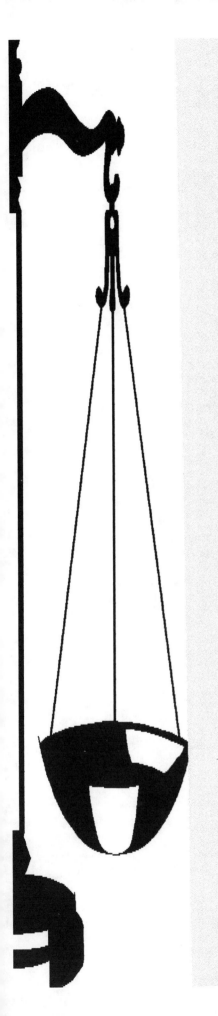

360 Degree #3

Guidelines for Understanding Criteria in Completing the "Factors and Methods Affecting Work Results" Area of the PA Form

The reverse side of the Performance Appraisal Form identifies several factors an methods that may affect your work results. Your performance will be evaluated on those factors that had and will continue to have the greatest impact on your contribution to the organization. Your supervisor will evaluate them as follows:

<u>**Meets Expectations (ME)**</u>

You are meeting the expectation for this factor.

<u>**Exceeds Expectations (EE)**</u>

You are exceeding the expectations for this factor.

<u>**Development Opportunity (DO)**</u>

This identifier may be used for one of three reasons:

1. You may need specific development in this area in order to meet job expectations, -or-
2. Your performance in this area meets expectations, but further development will enhance your contribution, -or-
3. Your performance in this area meets or exceeds expectations, but new opportunities exist for applying these attributes.

Considerations to be used when evaluating each of the following work factors and methods:

Knowledge - Consider the degree to which the individual has attained and continues to acquire the job knowledge necessary to perform the duties essential to the present job.

Planning/Organizing - Consider the ability to plan, schedule, and organize work to make more effective use of time, materials, equipment , and other resources. Also, consider the ability to establish realistic goals and workable course of action.

Analysis - consider the ability to a) take a complex situation and reduce it to significant components in a logical, systematic manner; b) recognize and anticipate problems and opportunities which may not be readily apparent; c) quickly identify significant information; d) identify and verify the cause of the problem; e) consistently use realistic approach to solving problems.

Creativity/Initiative - Consider the ability to recognize what needs to be done, originate or develop ideas, and get things started. Consider the ingenuity and creativity employed in solving or effectively handling difficult or unusual problems.

Cost Awareness - Consider the ability to control product, labor, material costs associated with job responsibilities.

Quality Orientation - Consider the degree to which quality objectives are applied in handling problems, projects, and other assigned work; also, consider the displayed commitment to seeking and making work

243

improvements.

Dependability - Consider the extent to which practices, instructions, and regulations are followed.

Interpersonal Skills/Communications - Consider the ability to a) actively listen; b) effectively present ideas and other information orally; c) effectively express ideas and issues clearly (verbal & written); d) provide and accept appropriate feedback.

Leadership - Consider the ability to a) create and maintain a work climate that stimulates individuals to contribute new ideas in a spirit of teamwork; b)provide effective work direction for subordinates or peers; c) set challenging goals, establish clear expectations, and measure accomplishments; d) diligently support company policies; e) maintain poise under pressure.

Versatility - Consider the effectiveness of work performed in an environment of changing conditions based on business demands.

Teamwork/Relationships with Others - Consider a) work habits affecting the morale and job satisfaction within the unit/team; b) the ability to work with, train, and/or develop team members and other personnel where applicable; c) the ability to establish trust and openness with others.

Timeliness - Consider the ability to meet and beat deadlines associated with work assignments and special projects.

Continuous Improvement - Consider the ability to seek new and better ways to do job; aspiring to high levels of performance. Demonstrates a willingness to change and supports/ encourages tothers to be innovative.

Customer Service - Consider the extent to which the employee effectively thinks and acts in support of the customer, internal or external. Meets customer needs in the most effective manner possible, by providing timely response and resolution of customer problems.

Others Factors - Consider any other factors that affect the results of the individual's or team's efforts.

For Managers and Supervisors:

Team Building - Fosters a cohesive, supportive work environment. Enhances employee morale through use of feedback and recognition. Gives credit where due. Sets a model that reflects highest work ethic and integrity.

Coaching/Guiding - Identifies employee development needs and provides training, coaching, and career guidance. Focuses on situation or behavior, not person or personalities.

Performance Management - Guides employees in setting goals and expectations, conducts progress reviews and performance evaluations in a timely and effective manner.

Delegation/Accessibility - Prioritizes and assigns work effectively. Organizes staff and delegates responsibility to empower employees to meet department objectives. Maintians open door policy and is accessible and available to employees as needed.

EXHIBIT C
<u>EMPLOYEE INPUT FORM</u>

In order to assist your supervisor in summarizing your performance appraisal, please complete this form and submit directly to your supervisor. (Completion of this form is optional.)

What do you consider to be your major accomplishments versus the expectations/goals of your job?

What expectations/goals were not completed?

Completed By: _____   Date:

EXHIBIT D
<u>PEER INPUT FORM</u>

Employee Being Reviewed: _____

Supervisor Requesting: _____

An important component of the company performance appraisal process is peer input. This underlies the tremendous importance our company places on working effectively together with a sharp focus on "the customer" both internally and externally. Please take a few minutes to complete this form and return promptly to the requesting supervisor.

Briefly describe the strengths of your working interface with the employee:

Briefly describe from your perspective, the areas needing to be improved in order to help the individual enhance their contribution:

Completed By: _____   **Date:** _____

SUBORDINATE INPUT FORM

Employee being Reviewed: _____

Supervisor/Manager Requesting: _____

Complete this form if the employee that you are providing input for is your manager or supervisor.

Areas to consider:

Communications: How well does my manager/supervisor listen, communicate (written and verbal) and provide effective and timely communications to team members.

Team Building: How well does my manager/supervisor foster a cohesive, supportive work environment and enhance employee morale through use of feedback and recognition.

Team Member Development: How well does my manager/supervisor identify employee development needs and provide training, coaching, and career guidance.

Performance Management: How well does my manager/supervisor guide the team in setting goals and expectations and conduct progress reviews and performance evaluations in a timely and effective manner.

Delegation/Accessibility: How well does my manager/supervisor prioritize and assign work effectively. How well does he/she organize staff and delegate responsibility to empower the team to meet department objectives? How available is he/she to the team?

Completed by: _____ Date: _____

EXHIBIT G
PERSONAL DEVELOPMENT PLAN

What are your plans to enhance effectiveness in your current assignment?

With your current education and experience, do you believe you could make a greater contribution to the Company in another position?_____ If so, name the position (s). _____

What are your career aspirations?

What knowledge/skills/experience would you need to develop to enhance the probability of achieving your career aspirations?

What are your plans to obtain the knowledge/skills/experience indicated above?

How can your supervisor or manager assist you with the achievement of your goals?

Name: _____   Date: _____

EXHIBIT A
ꓭAL SETTING FORM

ANTITY & QUALITY)   TARGET DATE

INDIVIDUAL GOALS:

ACCOMPLISHMENT (QUANTITY & QUALITY)   TARGET DATE

1.

2.

3.

4.

5.

_____   _____   _____   _____
EMPLOYEE'S SIGNATURE   DATE   SUPERVISOR'S SIGNATURE   DATE

Page 11

EXHIBIT B
PROGRESS REVIEW FORM

Review Period_____

PROGRESS ON TEAM GOALS

_____

PROGRESS ON INDIVIDUAL GOALS

_____

| EMPLOYEE'S SIGNATURE | DATE | SUPERVISOR'S SIGNATURE | DATE |

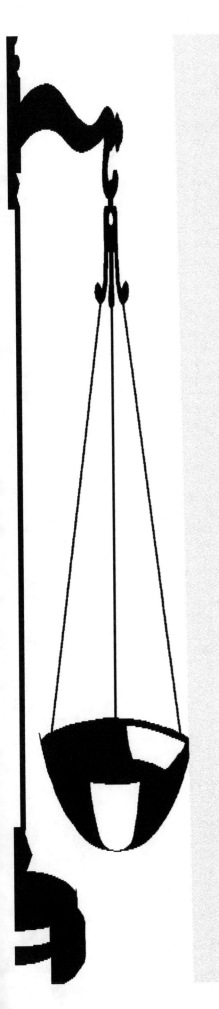

360 Degree #4

EMPLOYEE ASSESSMENT QUESTIONNAIRE

Employee Name:_____   Evaluator Name:_____

In preparation for your upcoming performance review, please answer the following questions with as much detail as you feel is necessary. Your answers will serve as a basis for discussion with me in planning your career development with IFS.

To Be Returned By :_____.

1. What achievements do you feel you have made during this past review period? In which areas do you feel you exceeded your position's standards and/or my expectations (be specific):

    _____

    _____

    _____

    _____

2. What aspects of your performance or skill level do you wish to improve (or focus on) during the next review period? In which areas do you see the benchmark or standard moving up for your job standards now that you have another year of experience and job knowledge (be specific):

    _____

    _____

    _____

    _____

3. What skills or knowledge will you be developing in order to achieve the improvements you've outlined above? How do you plan to gain these skills/knowledge?

    _____

    _____

    _____

    _____

4. What longer range goals do you see for yourself in your current position or for your career at IFS?

    _____

    _____

    _____

MANAGEMENT

For HRD use only:
Overall Rating _____
Review Points _____
Discussion Date ___/___/___
Next Review Date ___/___/___

☐ 90 Day
☐ Annual

Employee Performance Appraisal

EMPLOYEE DATA

NAME: _____

JOB TITLE: _____

HIRE DATE: ___/___/___   DATE IN POSITION: ___/___/___

REVIEW PERIOD: FROM ___/___/___ TO ___/___/___

PREPARED BY: _____ DATE PREPARED: ___/___/___

The evaluator's immediate supervisor and Human Resources must review the contents of the appraisal before the appraisal review session is conducted with the employee.

NEXT LEVEL APPROVAL: _____ DATE: ___/___/___

H.R. APPROVAL: _____ DATE: ___/___/___

I participated in this Employee Performance Appraisal with my supervisor on the date indicated. The content of this review has been discussed with me in detail. My signature indicates knowledge and understanding of the contents of the appraisal and does not necessarily imply agreement.

EMPLOYEE SIGNATURE: _____ DATE: ___/___/___

EVALUATOR SIGNATURE: _____ DATE: ___/___/___

Levels of Performance

OUTSTANDING	Performance and results achieved <u>always exceed the standards and expectations</u> for the position requirements, standards and long & short-term objectives.
EXCEEDS STANDARDS	Performance and results achieved <u>consistently exceed the standards and expectations</u> for the position requirements, standards and long & short-term objectives.
MEETS STANDARDS	Performance and results achieved <u>generally meet the standards and expectations</u> for the position requirements, standards and long & short-term objectives.
BELOW STANDARDS	Performance and results achieved <u>generally do not meet the standards and expectations</u> for the position requirements, standards and long & short-term objectives.
UNSATISFACTORY	Performance and results achieved <u>consistently do not meet the standards and expectations</u> for the position requirements, standards and long & short-term objectives.

255

OPERATIONAL RESPONSIBILITIES AND OBJECTIVES

(To be completed and signed at beginning of rating period.)

Briefly describe the major expectations, responsibilities, objectives, goals or assignments and position standards for the coming review period. Assign each objective A, B, or C priority and a target completion date.

ACTUAL ACHIEVEMENTS

(To be completed and signed at end of rating period.)

Describe the employee's performance and results achieved on those previously agreed-upon objectives, position standards, and responsibilities as listed at the beginning of the rating period.

(circle one)

Priority: A B C

1. Objective: Target Completion Date:

Achievement:

(1)___Unsatisfacorty   (2)___Below Standards   (3)___Meets Standards   (4)___Exceeds Standards   (5)___Outstanding

---

(circle one)

Priority: A B C

2. Objective: Target Completion Date:

Achievement:

(1)___Unsatisfacorty   (2)___Below Standards   (3)___Meets Standards   (4)___Exceeds Standards   (5)___Outstanding

---

256

3. Objective:

Priority: A B C
Target Completion Date:

Achievement:

(1)___Unsatisfacotry   (2)___Below Standards   (3)___Meets Standards   (4)___Exceeds Standards   (5)___Outstanding

Priority: A B C
Target Completion Date:

4. Objective:

Achievement:

(1)___Unsatisfacotry   (2)___Below Standards   (3)___Meets Standards   (4)___Exceeds Standards   (5)___Outstanding

Priority: A B C
Target Completion Date:

5. Objective:

Achievement:

(1)___Unsatisfacotry   (2)___Below Standards   (3)___Meets Standards   (4)___Exceeds Standards   (5)___Outstanding

MANAGEMENT PRACTICES

(Based on the individual's effectiveness and sensitivity as a manager complete the following evaluation summations. Assign each factor A, B, or C priority.)

PERFORMANCE FACTORS

ACCOUNTABILITY

(circle one)

Priority: A B C

Accepts responsibility for decisions, whatever the outcomes are. Constructively questions why we do things certain ways. Looks for, and evaluates, alternatives. solicits and encourages ideas from subordinates, peers, superiors, etc. Acknowledges originators of ideas. Seeks greater responsibility, but not to a fault. Is a decision maker. Requires little supervision. Is self-confident. Recommends actions. Acts in boss's absence. Resists group pressure, in defense of convictions.

Evaluation Summation:

(1)____Unsatisfactory   (2)____Below Standards   (3)____Meets Standards   (4)____Exceeds Standards   (5)____Outstanding

ANALYSIS

(circle one)

Priority: A B C

Analyzes - Identifies problems, secures relevant information, relates data from different sources and identifies possible causes of problems and takes corrective action. Judgment - Develops alternate courses of action and makes decisions based on logical assumptions and factual information.

Evaluation Summation:

(1)____Unsatisfactory   (2)____Below Standards   (3)____Meets Standards   (4)____Exceeds Standards   (5)____Outstanding

ASSERTIVENESS (not aggressiveness)

(circle one)

Priority: A B C

Is direct, honest, behaves appropriately and does not step on others in the process. Allows for full utilization of all resources. Stands up for personal rights and expresses thoughts, feelings, and preferences in a way that is direct, honest, appropriate, and does not violate the rights of others. Assertiveness involves respect instead of deference. Assertiveness involves two kinds of respect: 1) Self respect - expression of rights, humanness, without feeling guilty (not to be confused with egotism, which is a position of superiority rather than equality); 2) Respect for the rights of Others - expression that is fair to others and does not limit their power to exercise their rights.

Evaluation Summation:

(1)____Unsatisfactory   (2)____Below Standards   (3)____Meets Standards   (4)____Exceeds Standards   (5)____Outstanding

BUDGET

(circle one)

Priority: A B C

Plans responsibly for departmental budgeted areas through careful projection of future expenses, monitoring of ongoing expenditures, and a continual demonstration of commitment to cost effectiveness and cost savings.

Evaluation Summation:

(1)____Unsatisfactory   (2)____Below Standards   (3)____Meets Standards   (4)____Exceeds Standards   (5)____Outstanding

COMMITMENT TO COMPANY GOALS

(circle one)
Priority: A B C

Is familiar with and displays support for corporate goals and objectives. Communicates the company vision to peers and subordinates and enlists support for achievement of these goals. Examines the value of projects/tasks in relation to how the project/task with help fulfill achievement of corporate goals before implementation is underway. Seldom hesitates to give whatever extra effort is necessary to meet desired goals and objectives.

Evaluation Summation:

(1)____Unsatisfactory (2)____Below Standards (3)____Meets Standards (4)____Exceeds Standards (5)____Outstanding

---

COMPENSATION

(circle one)
Priority: A B C

Recognizes and provides for direct relationship between individual employee performance and compensation; plans for and allocates compensation dollars in fair and equitable manner using sound managerial judgment in the application of the guidelines. Employees receive timely review and merit increase.

Evaluation Summation:

(1)____Unsatisfactory (2)____Below Standards (3)____Meets Standards (4)____Exceeds Standards (5)____Outstanding

---

ENTREPRENEUR/RISK TAKING

(circle one)
Priority: A B C

Thinks independently - acts corporately. Takes calculated risks. Makes difficult commitments. Makes good decisions with limited facts when necessary.

Evaluation Summation:

(1)____Unsatisfactory (2)____Below Standards (3)____Meets Standards (4)____Exceeds Standards (5)____Outstanding

---

INTERNAL CUSTOMER SERVICE/SATISFACTION

(circle one)
Priority: A B C

Consults with internal resources. Measures and reports on internal customer satisfaction. Identifies the customers and their goals and needs - what can be contributed. Is sensitive to how others are impacted by what the department does, or decisions that are made.

Evaluation Summation:

(1)____Unsatisfactory (2)____Below Standards (3)____Meets Standards (4)____Exceeds Standards (5)____Outstanding

259

LEADERSHIP

(circle one)
Priority: A B C

Utilizes appropriate management practices and methods in guiding individuals or groups toward task accomplishment. Focuses on the end result, does not get lost in the tasks, maintains a vision of the goal.

Evaluation Summation:

(1)____Unsatisfactory   (2)____Below Standards   (3)____Meets Standards   (4)____Exceeds Standards   (5)____Outstanding

---

MANAGEMENT DEVELOPMENT *(Self-Subordinates-Peers-Superiours)*

(circle one)
Priority: A B C

Selects good people by establishing thorough, job related selection criteria and carefully screens to meet those criteria. Trains employees by having development plans in effect for subordinates and self. Coaches and makes available training opportunities and necessary resources. Informs employees of the company's expectations, performance-assessment process and employee development plans. Executes organizational planning, effective replacement or succession planning and growth-need planning.

Evaluation Summation:

(1)____Unsatisfactory   (2)____Below Standards   (3)____Meets Standards   (4)____Exceeds Standards   (5)____Outstanding

---

MEETINGS

(circle one)
Priority: A B C

Conducts meetings and appropriately utilizes "decks". Clearly defines the meeting purpose and objective. Plans an agenda, summarizes meeting results and follows up with delegated tasks. Participation - punctual, commits to goal of meeting, makes participative contributions.

Evaluation Summation:

(1)____Unsatisfactory   (2)____Below Standards   (3)____Meets Standards   (4)____Exceeds Standards   (5)____Outstanding

---

PROACTIVE PLANNING AND ORGANIZING

(circle one)
Priority: A B C

(Anticipates-Initiative-Delegation)

Anticipates alternate events and establishes courses of action for self and/or others to accomplish specific objectives; plans proper assignments of personnel and/or appropriate allocation of resources. Makes active attempts to influence events to secure organizational supplies, resources or information to achieve objectives. Utilizes subordinates and other resources effectively. Allocates decision making and other responsibilities to the appropriate subordinates.

Evaluation Summation:

(1)____Unsatisfactory   (2)____Below Standards   (3)____Meets Standards   (4)____Exceeds Standards   (5)____Outstanding

PROFESSIONALISM *(Image-Value System)*

Priority: A B C

Patient, calm, empathetic, resolute, positive, courageous, dependable, committed to getting the job done, discrete. Image - is appropriately attired, composed, punctual, a communicator, knowledgeable of the business, involved in outside interests self-confident. Value system - has a value system compatible with the company's. supports company's value system.

Evaluation Summation:

(1)___Unsatisfactory (2)___Below Standards (3)___Meets Standards (4)___Exceed Standards (5)___Outstanding

---

SAFETY

(circle one)

Priority: A B C

Recognizes the importance of safety concerns and guidelines, makes staff aware of same and holds them accountable for following safety procedures.

Evaluation Summation:

(1)___Unsatisfactory (2)___Below Standards (3)___Meets Standards (4)___Exceeds Standards (5)___Outstanding

---

TEAMWORK *(Trust-positive behavior)*

(circle one)

Priority: A B C

Works with others for the common good of all and tolerates differences. Strives to set team and group objectives as well as individual objectives that are in concert with overall IFS objectives. Conducts team meetings for subordinates and peers that serve to increase trust, mutual respect, motivation and growth. Is helpful and supportive in daily contacts with subordinates and peers. Demonstrates enthusiasm for IFS goals. Demonstrates positive behavior by suggesting possible solutions, alternatives and new methods. Focuses on "How To".

Evaluation Summation:

(1)___Unsatisfactory (2)___Below Standards (3)___Meets Standards (4)___Exceeds Standards (5)___Outstanding

---

WORK DIRECTION

(circle one)

Priority: A B C

Provides information and encouragement necessary to get work done; advises and counsels subordinates to help them initiate action to correct problems. Identifies what needs to be done; sets priorities; matches people to jobs; delegates fairly; prepares necessary schedules, and balances task requirements against work morale and work loads.

Evaluation Summation:

(1)___Unsatisfactory (2)___Below Standards (3)___Meets Standards (4)___Exceeds Standards (5)___Outstanding

OVERALL PERFORMANCE RATING
The rating should be based on performance in all areas of responsibility since the last review.

(1)____Unsatisfactory*   (2)____Below Standards*   (3)____Meets Standards   (4)____Exceeds Standards   (5)____Outstanding

* (ineligible for increase)

COMMENTS ON LEVEL CHOSEN AND PERFORMANCE ORIENTED STRENGTHS
Comments should consider demonstration of skills, abilities, and efforts required to achieve results, as well as exceptional circumstances that had an impact on results. Describe the individual's most significant performance - oriented strengths.

AREAS FOR IMPROVEMENT
Describe areas where performance could be improved.

EMPLOYEE'S COMMENTS AND RECOMMENDATIONS

Dear_____,

I would appreciate your assistance in completing this brief questionnaire. The purpose of this exercise is to gain insight into the perceptions on my leadership effectiveness. The questions you will be responding to carefully reflect the core values and management practices of IFS. These values are:

- Customer Satisfaction
- Integrity
- Commitment to Excellence
- Profitable Growth
- Employee Satisfaction
- Innovation & Adaptability
- Trust & Mutual Respect
- Teamwork
- Leadership
- FUN!

This is a 360 degree process which seeks input from subordinate, supervisory and peer level associates. This anonymous data will be tabulated by Kleinfelder, Incorporated, a firm that IFS has hired to tabulate the data, prepare reports and assist in the developmental process with myself and my manager. You will direct this survey to Kleinfelder by returning your feedback in the enclosed self-addressed, stamped envelope. This survey will be destroyed once it is tabulated by the Kleinfelder Organization. I will receive a report summarizing the perceptions in the skill areas contained in this survey (without names) so that I can develop action plans for my personal improvement goals.

The survey is designed for completion in 12 minutes or less. Please return the survey by _____. Again, thank you in advance for taking time out of your busy schedule to assist me in this worthwhile process. If you have any questions about this survey process, please contact Dory Gouge-Gericke, Vice President of Human Resources at ext. 2164.

Thank you.

_____
Participant's Signature

LEADERSHIP QUALITIES

Please check the box that best describes your perception of the participant's skill level.

If you are unsure of an area, leave it blank.

I. PERSONAL QUALITIES	Never	Sometimes	Often	Always
Reflects IFS values and management practices in style and personal actions				
Direct, honest, respects and acknowledges the contribution of others				
Confident in self and gives personal best				
Confident in and seeks the best from others				
Does what is necessary to get the job done				
Ethical				
Reliable in meeting commitments to others				
Displays a positive attitude; enthusiastic				
Respects and maintains confidentiality; trustworthy				
Sets example of delivering exceptional customer service				
Comments:				

II. CHANGE MASTERY	Never	Sometimes	Often	Always
Displays vision and a keen sense of the future; sees emerging opportunities				
Generates new ideas and process improvements				
Attempts to influence organizational events; versus reacting to them				
Thinks independently; takes calculated risks				
Utilizes resources internal to the organization				
Questions the way things are done				
Presents positive solutions to organizational challenges				
Builds commitment by looking for the common ground				
Understands, supports and effectively communicates changes to employees and/or customers				
Comments:				

III. COMMUNICATION	Never	Sometimes	Often	Always
Provides clear, concise verbal directions and explanations				
Expresses self effectively before individuals and groups				
Demonstrates respect for other points of view; empathetic; seeks clarification; highlights areas of agreement				
Listens with genuine interest and reflects back feelings				
Sensitive to non-verbal cues				
Encourages the free expression of opinions without being defensive				
Clearly expresses ideas in writing and uses correct grammatical form				
Can influence others to embrace a position; persuasive				
Can think quickly and respond to challenges raised by others in a tactful, positive manner				
Knows when to disengage and when to withdraw; avoids personal discomfort				
Comments:				

IV. DECISION-MAKING	Never	Sometimes	Often	Always
Strives for brevity, clarity and appropriate solutions				
Identifies problems, secures relevant information and assimilates data				
Anticipates problems and opportunities				
Seeks advice from others when appropriate				
Makes decisions and renders judgments in a timely manner based on facts				
Decisions balance company's profitability and customer needs				
Applies intuitive thinking when necessary				
Applies strategic thinking for leadership role				
Comments:				

V. RESILIENCE	Never	Sometimes	Often	Always
Embraces disappointments, learns from mistakes and takes future risks				
Accepts diversity of opinions; unafraid to let people speak their minds; solicits different views				
Handles pressure and multiple demands				
Defends personal opinions				
Accepts responsibility for actions and will not blame others				
Stays with position or plan until the desired objective is achieved; persistent				
Comments:				

VI. BUSINESS KNOWLEDGE	Never	Sometimes	Often	Always
Understands IFS financial performance indicators				
Understands IFS culture				
Understands the fundraising industry and IFS business practice				
Understands the competition				
Knows how to gain competitive advantage				
Understands and meets customer's expectations				
Understands and meets sponsor's expectations				
Understands, supports and meets FRD's needs				
Comments:				

VII. TEAM COMMITMENT	Never	Sometimes	Often	Always
Demonstrates willingness to act in best interests of IFS				
Works with others for the common good and tolerates differences				
Strives to set team and group objectives consistent with IFS goals				
Fosters trust and mutual respect in team meetings				
Helpful and supportive in daily contacts with subordinates and peers				
Supportive of other departmental goals; willing to lend assistance				
Asks for help when needed				
Admits mistakes; minimizes blame to others				
Comments:				

VIII. MANAGEMENT	Never	Sometimes	Often	Always
Selects good people				
Trains and develops employees				
Conducts regular coaching discussions and staff meetings				
Builds strength and continuity in the team				
Handles conflict; resolves performance problems				
Consistent and timely in giving performance reviews				
Anticipates future events; planning				
Sets challenging goals for self and others				
Allocates decision-making responsibilities to appropriate staff				
Establishes performance expectation standards				
Comments:				

IX. LEADERSHIP	Never	Sometimes	Often	Always
Sets clear expectations and establishes direction				
Frequently shares information about the organizational direction				
Maximizes the individual talents on the team				
Treats people fairly				
Brings out the best in people; understands motivational needs				
Energizes people towards a common objective				
Displays flexibility in management style				
Reinforces positive performance				
Appropriately involves/includes the right people				
Leads by influence and example				
Comments:				

1.   What three goals do you think _____ should focus on developing?

    a)

    b)

    c)

Please return this form in the enclosed envelope. Thank you.

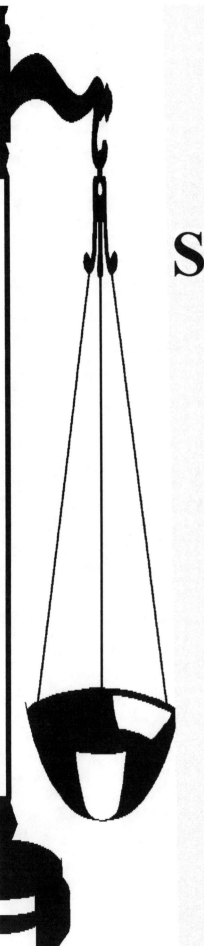

XII.

Seasonal Appraisal

SEASONAL EMPLOYEE APPRAISAL

RATE EACH CATEGORY SEPARATELY -- Include comments as needed.

ES   MS   BS

(ES = Exceeds Standards   MS = Meets Standards   BS = Below Standards)

A.   **JOB KNOWLEDGE & COMPREHENSION:** Is knowledgeable of the duties methods and procedures required by the job.

A.

_____

_____

B.   **WORK QUALITY:** Understands and meets work standards in an accurate, prompt neat manner, including standards for verbal/written communications, if applicable.

B.

_____

_____

C.   **PRODUCTIVITY:** Consistently produces required volume of work. Maintains attention to work and meets deadlines.

C.

_____

_____

D.   **ACCURACY:** Identifies and corrects errors. Is careful, alert and accurate, paying attention to details of the job.

D.

_____

_____

E.   **WORK HABITS:** Demonstrates commitment, dedication, teamwork, positive attitude, initiative and flexibility with changes in jobs and duties.

E.

_____

_____

F.   **INTERPERSONAL SKILLS:** Demonstrates ability to get along with others, is respectful of co-workers, communicates and acts as a team player.

F.

_____

_____

G.   **ATTENDANCE & PUNCTUALITY:** Dependable, arrives at work on time, reports on all scheduled days, adheres to break and meal schedules.
NUMBER OF OCCURRENCES: **Absences** _____   **Tardies** _____

G.

_____

_____

ELIGIBLE FOR REHIRE:
(In your department)   ☐ Y   ☐ N   ☐ Conditional*

TOTAL OVERALL RATING:

ES   MS   BS

* Explain:

_____

_____

Name/EE #:   Evaluator: _____

Supervisor:

Dept.:   Date: ____/____/____

Season: